LIFE SCIENCE LIBRARY

MACHINES

OTHER BOOKS
BY THE
EDITORS OF LIFE

LIFE SCIENCE LIBRARY

CONSULTING EDITORS
René Dubos
Henry Margenau
C. P. Snow

MACHINES

by Robert O'Brien
and the Editors of LIFE

TIME INCORPORATED, NEW YORK

A
STONEHENGE
BOOK

THE AUTHOR

ROBERT O'BRIEN is a veteran journalist who has increasingly applied his talents to investigating and explaining developments in the world of science. His magazine articles, covering fields from computer technology to mental disease, have appeared in LIFE, *Esquire, Reader's Digest, Collier's* and in several anthologies. For 13 years a newspaperman and columnist for the San Francisco *Chronicle*, he is the author of two historical books about the West, *This Is San Francisco* and *California Called Them*.

THE CONSULTING EDITORS

RENE DUBOS, member and professor of The Rockefeller Institute, is a microbiologist and experimental pathologist world-famous for his pioneering in antibiotics, including the discovery of tyrothricin. He has written, among other books, *Mirage of Health* and *The Dreams of Reason*.

HENRY MARGENAU is Eugene Higgins professor of physics and natural philosophy at Yale and an editor of the *American Journal of Science*. His books include *Open Vistas* and *The Nature of Physical Reality*. He has made noteworthy contributions in spectroscopy and nuclear physics.

C. P. SNOW has won an international audience for his novels, including *The New Men, The Search* and *The Affair*, which explore the scientist's role in our society. Trained as a physicist, he was chief of scientific personnel for Britain's Ministry of Labour in World War II. He was knighted in 1957.

ON THE COVER

The delicately meshed clockwork of a fine Swiss watch and the piston *(back cover)* represent patrician and workhorse in man's still-expanding repertory of machines. A culmination of 450 years of watchmaker's precision tooling, this pocket watch has nine hands and five dials, and chimes the hour, quarter hour and minutes to communicate the exact time.

CONTENTS

TIME INC. BOOK DIVISION

EDITOR
Norman P. Ross

COPY DIRECTOR
William Jay Gold

ART DIRECTOR
Edward A. Hamilton

CHIEF OF RESEARCH
Beatrice T. Dobie

EDITORIAL STAFF FOR "MACHINES"

EDITOR, LIFE SCIENCE LIBRARY: George McCue
TEXT EDITOR: Diana Hirsh
ASSISTANT TO THE EDITOR: Robert G. Mason
DESIGNER: Arnold C. Holeywell
ASSOCIATE DESIGNER: Edwin Taylor
STAFF WRITERS: Stephen Espie,
    Harvey B. Loomis, Paul Trachtman
CHIEF RESEARCHER: Sheila Osmundsen
RESEARCHERS: Norbert S. Baer, Doris C. Coffin,
    Mollie Cooper, Elizabeth Evans, Owen Fang, Emily Heine,
    John L. Hochmann, Leonard Lipton, Robert R. McLaughlin,
    Renée Pickèl, Victor H. Waldrop, Dori Watson
PICTURE RESEARCHERS: Margaret K. Goldsmith, Joan Lynch
ART ASSOCIATE: Robert L. Young
ART ASSISTANTS: James D. Smith, W. Lee Einhorn,
    Charles Mikolaycak, Douglas B. Graham
COPY STAFF: Marian Gordon Goldman,
    Suzanne Seixas, Dolores A. Littles

PUBLISHER: Jerome S. Hardy
GENERAL MANAGER: John A. Watters

LIFE MAGAZINE

EDITOR: Edward K. Thompson
MANAGING EDITOR: George P. Hunt
PUBLISHER: C. D. Jackson

The text for the chapters of this book was written by Robert O'Brien, for
the picture essays by the editorial staff. The following individuals and de-
partments of Time Inc. were helpful in the production of the book: Larry
Burrows, Ralph Crane, Alfred Eisenstaedt and Dmitri Kessel, LIFE staff
photographers; Margaret Sargent, LIFE film editor; Doris O'Neil, Chief of
the LIFE Picture Library; Philip Payne of the TIME-LIFE News Service;
and Content Peckham, Chief, Time Inc. Bureau of Editorial Reference.

INTRODUCTION

MY GRANDFATHER, the Henry Ford who made the Model T and mass production famous, was a man who drew a sharp distinction between working hard and doing hard work. He believed very strongly in the former, and very little in the latter.

His boyhood on a 19th Century farm convinced him that men and horses were doing a lot of hard work that could and should be done by machines. It was a conviction that dominated his life, and brought him into the pages of this LIFE book, which is about the machines that man has devised both to make his work easier and to do what man, unassisted, can't do at all.

Since my grandfather's birth a century ago, machines have transformed daily living. We have, as he himself put it, "taken the heavy labor from man's back and placed it on the broad back of the machine." But machines mean much more to us than just easing our daily burden. The really significant thing about a machine is not that it allows a man to do a given job in half the time, but that it can also allow a man to *produce* twice as much in a given time.

My grandfather won a place in history by putting that concept to work. He demonstrated that increased production lowers the cost of goods so more people can afford them. It was an idea that revolutionized the Industrial Revolution.

Even in his day, some people were concerned that machines were doing more *to* us than *for* us. But my grandfather never worried about the possibility of over-mechanization. "The machine has brought actual equality between men," he said. "The critics of the machine are out of date. Instead of less machinery there will be more."

Time has borne out his prediction. We have had more machinery, and it has given us constantly better material living and more leisure in which to enjoy it. But of course times have also changed. A leapfrogging technology has given us instruments of such complexity and capability that again the question is being asked: Have we, this time, finally gone too far with our machines?

Personally, I'll string along with my grandfather.

Along with the benefits they bring, today's machines pose problems which I don't discount. It is essential that we concern ourselves with solving them. But in the long view, we cannot continue to prosper unless we continue to increase our productivity, and we can increase our productivity only by embracing all the technological advance that science makes possible.

This book shows how far man has come in using his God-given gifts to improve the conditions of his life. It can only hint at how much farther we should be able to go.

—HENRY FORD II

1

The Machine-made Fabric of the American Dream

IMAGINE FOR A NIGHTMARISH MOMENT what it would be like if by some vast, automated whim all our machines—simple and complex, muscle-powered as well as electronic—suddenly went on strike.

Our lives would grind abruptly, clumsily, comically, tragically, overwhelmingly to a standstill. We would be unable to tell time, wash, shave, cook, open cans, turn on lights, heat the house, mow the lawn, telephone, listen to the radio, watch television, go anyplace or do anything most of us consider worth doing.

Across the wide, silent, smog-free continent, 83 million cars, trucks, buses and tractors would stand frozen. No assembly lines would assemble in Detroit, no smoke feather over St. Louis. Canaveral would belong once more to the sea, sun, sand and gulls. *Nautilus* would lie incommunicado beneath the sea. SAC would be grounded. All of us would be cut off from the world, from the next town—from each other.

Machines have been a basic part of our heritage. While still a wilderness, our republic was a commonwealth of farmer-mechanics. A century ago Ralph Waldo Emerson noted that his countrymen took to the newfangled steam train "as if it were the cradle in which they were born." Today mere youngsters pull hot rods apart and put them back together again. Our native genius for invention and for just plain tinkering of the jackknife-and-baling-wire variety has made many machines what they are. In return, machines have fabricated the American dream into reality. Now we could not survive without each other.

Machines provide the means through which matter's conversion into energy is made available for man's use. They place at our finger tips the might of wind and falling water, the force of steam and thunderbolt. They make it possible to pack the strength of 400 horses beneath the hood of a car, to cram the fury of 24 million obliterating tons of TNT into a single bomb. They give us the power to compress time and all but annihilate space.

A man cannot budge a boulder with his bare hands. Yet when he pushes a crowbar beneath it, props a rock under the crowbar to serve as fulcrum, then pries upward, the boulder moves. Crowbar and fulcrum form a lever, giving him what physicists call "mechanical advantage," enabling his limited resources of strength to overcome the boulder's resistance. With his hands a man may just about crumple a beer can; but at his merest touch on a control, a hydraulic press will squeeze a 1,200-pound steel automobile body into a tight bale the size of a school desk. With a good throwing arm, a man can skim a stone a distance of 100 feet; but by pushing a button he can make a machine hurl a 150-ton rocket, with payload, 6,500 miles down the Atlantic range to the bull's-eye of a predetermined target. An electronic machine accomplishes in seconds calculations which he could not perform in years. A winged machine

A DUALITY OF POWER AND PARTS
All machinery ever invented would remain a silent mass of useless parts without a source of power, whether muscular or atomic. The more man controls the energy of his power sources, the more disciplined his machines become. One of these, the electric-powered shaper *(opposite)*, can shave an ingot with such controlled force that absence of vibration leaves a nickel standing.

flies him nearly a quarter of the way around the world in the time it takes him to hike 30 miles.

Just what is a machine? Although by now an inextricable part of our lives, it is surprisingly hard to define. When Professor Franz Reuleaux, the renowned German engineer, wrote his classic *Kinematics of Machinery* in 1875, he listed 15 definitions drafted by distinguished fellow professionals in France, Germany and Italy. No two were alike.

The word "machine" itself is derived from the Greek *mechane* and its Latin cognate *machina*. Both mean, loosely, "any ingenious device or invention," which helps us not at all. Webster's New International Dictionary says that a machine is "Any device consisting of two or more resistant, relatively constrained parts, which, by a certain predetermined intermotion, may serve to transmit and modify force and motion so as to produce some given effect or to do some desired kind of work." This is an excellent definition, but specialized, with a bias toward the mechanical engineer. It can, without dispute, be broadened to include all mechanical and electronic devices that extend or refine human powers.

A durable quintet

Although machines have multiplied vastly over the centuries, even the most up-to-the-minute list must begin with five devices enumerated by the Greek inventive genius, Hero of Alexandria, about the time of Christ: the lever, the wheel and axle, the pulley, the wedge and the screw. Even though they do not meet the dictionary definition that a machine must have "two or more" parts, these tools are viewed as "simple machines"—detachable extensions of the human body that, in the main, supplement the functions of arms. Variations of Hero's elementary quintet are everywhere around us. A shovel, for example, is a modified lever. A chisel is a sharp wedge. An auger is a screw.

In addition to tools, any consideration of machines should also include "prime movers": mechanisms—or organisms—that convert a natural form of energy into another form capable of producing motion. The body extracts chemical energy from food and converts it into muscular energy that enables the human being to talk, walk, swing a golf club. A waterwheel converts the kinetic energy of flowing water into power that spins a shaft. A steam engine converts the chemical energy in coal into the thermal energy of steam that drives a piston. A mechanical engineer might say that machines, as *receivers* of power from prime movers, belong in a separate category. Technically he would be correct. But to write about machines and leave out prime movers would be to deal in futilities: in automobile chassis without engines, as it were.

Man's discovery of such prime movers as windmills, along with his conquest of metal and his contrivance of the wheel, were the harbingers of today's mechanized world. But even as far back as paleolithic times, he had shown his proclivities as "the toolmaking animal," in Benjamin Franklin's celebrated phrase. He contrived keen-edged flint knives, weighted digging sticks, hand axes of patiently chipped quartz and harpoons tipped with piercing bone. All were savage appendages of his own hands, nails and teeth: in mechanical terms, primitive or proto-machines, simple devices for applying his strength more effectively. He used poles as levers to pry up rocks. He discovered that a deer's antler, bent and held taut by a sinew bowstring, would release its pent-up energy in a twanging burst when he let the string go, and would send an arrow to its mark. He found that a stick twirled between his hands made fire more quickly than two sticks rubbed together.

Thus man stumbled upon "simple machines" and began to perceive the powers they conferred. He found that levers provided mechanical advantage. In the bow he hit upon his first energy-storing device. The fire stick produced partial rotary motion.

Metal, the final, shining, forgeable, enduring substance of machines to come, effectively succumbed to man's will after he had turned from nomad to farmer in the valleys of Mesopotamia about 6000 B.C. He had long since utilized pure copper, but this was a rarity in nature; now, by a happy accident, he became aware that certain stones would magically bleed fine beads of the metal if heated with charcoal under forced draft. He learned how to work this molten copper into axes and chisels that he could sharpen when they grew dull. He was now freed from dependence upon stubborn stone for his implements.

Shades of a lazy susan

The next momentous advance in machine history was the wheel and axle. This great underpinning of all technology came along before 3000 B.C. Learning to shape clay into pots on a slab of wood that he could turn as his work progressed, man also learned to round off the slab for easier grasping, and raise it on a base—a bearing—so that he could spin it freely, as today we spin a lazy susan on our dinner table. In this manner he fashioned the potter's wheel, prototype of the wheel and axle, the solid wooden cart wheel, the spoked chariot wheel, the many millions of 20th Century wheels that carry us to and from work.

The first energy man exploited, other than that of his own body, was animal power. The usual method of raising irrigation water from a well or spring was by means of a vertical wheel, hung with pots that were fitted at an angle to the wheel's perimeter; the pots would scoop up the water at the bottom of the turn and spill it out into a sluice or trough as the wheel lifted them on high. The wheel itself was turned by endless human plodding on a treadmill. Sometime before the Christian era, some imag-

A POTENT PRIMITIVE TOOL

By combining muscle power and the *shaduf*, a type of lever, Egyptians lifted water from the Nile to irrigate farms above the river level. This sketch, based on a tomb painting of about 1500 B.C., shows a farmer lowering a cone-shaped leather bucket which hangs from a beam balanced across two pillars. The weight of the counterpoise fixed to the other end of the beam permitted the farmer to lift the filled bucket with less exertion.

inative Near East farmer wearied of this routine. He removed the tread-mill, added a second vertical wheel to the shaft of the wheel-of-pots, and fitted the circumference of this wheel with wooden pegs for teeth, pro-truding like handles on a ship's helm. He geared the toothed drive wheel to a similarly pegged horizontal wheel, to whose shaft he attached a beam. To the beam he hitched his ox. The ox toiled round and round, turning the beam, which rotated the horizontal wheel, which rotated the vertical wheel, whose shaft at last turned the wheel-of-pots.

This historic achievement was matched by another: the development of the sail, the first mechanism to harness natural power—the first non-living prime mover. Ingenious Egyptian boatmen, pushing their reed skiffs up the Nile, may have been the first to raise a patch of cloth and rest on their oars while they skimmed before the wind. In time, wooden cargo ships of the Pharaohs were faring as far north as Crete. The inno-cent look of them—long, trim, white-winged against the sea—was packed with explosive significance. Someday sails like these would take men to the rim of the world and beyond.

In the hills of the Fertile Crescent, about 100 B.C., another master craftsman invented another portentous contrivance. Customarily grain was ground between two heavy, disklike stones, one atop the other, with the bottom stone fixed; the top stone was rotated by means of hand bars protruding from its circumference. This innovator set his millstones on a horizontal wooden frame above a swift-running stream. To the center of the upper stone he fastened a vertical shaft, or axle. He ran the shaft through a hole in the center of the lower stone, which he fixed to the frame. To the bottom of the shaft he fastened a small, horizontal paddle wheel, which caught the edge of the current. The stream turned the pad-dle wheel, the shaft, the millstone—and thereby produced flour.

The importance of this prime mover, both for technology and for man-kind, cannot be overrated. Often called a Norse mill because of its later widespread use in northern Europe, it was the first mechanism to put to man's use the power of flowing water, the prototype of all water mills, the direct antecedent of today's giant turbines, a single one of which can manufacture enough electric power to serve 60,000 homes.

Advice to the toilworn

To the women of the Mediterranean uplands, who had never known a time when there was not grain to grind arduously by hand, the wa-ter mill was a boon, a delight. Wrote the poet Antipater of Thessalonica in the First Century B.C.: "Cease from grinding, ye women who toil at the mill; sleep late, even if the crowing cocks announce the dawn. For Demeter has ordered the Nymphs to perform the work of your hands, and they, leaping down on the top of the wheel, turn its axle which,

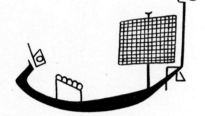

PROTOTYPE OF A TRAVELER

The oldest known depiction of a sail appears in this 5,000-year-old Egyptian drawing of a Nile river craft. According to one theory, the idea of harnessing the wind to propel a boat came to a bright sailor who noted that he no longer had to row his little reed skiff when the prevailing breeze caught his cloak. Indeed, the square sail appears to resemble a standing man whose loose garments hang from his outstretched arms.

with its revolving spokes, turns the heavy concave Nisyrian millstones."

Some five centuries later, perhaps at an oasis in the Persian province of Seistan, where searing winds blow across the salt deserts, another farmer-inventor devised a paddle wheel on a vertical shaft, and sank the end of the shaft into the center of his upper millstone. Having no stream of water to turn it, he raised it instead into the stream of air—and thus invented the windmill: another producer of rotary motion, another prime mover, another triumph over toil.

Crude contraptions? Awkward, creaking, cantankerous, inefficient, wooden barbarisms? By all means. Yet they were the beginning.

By the 14th and 15th Centuries, in England alone, new machines powered by waterwheels were crushing ore, sawing wood, pumping forge bellows, making paper and drawing wire. Across the Channel in what is now The Netherlands, some 8,000 high-sailed windmills drove saws, ground grain and powered pumps that reclaimed land from the sea. Since the average waterwheel and windmill of that time delivered between 5 and 10 horsepower, inhabitants of these two countries had at their disposal hundreds of thousands of prime-mover horsepower. Within another two centuries they were applying it to the intricate new labor-saving contrivances that could knit, spin thread, weave cloth and produce blast for smelting furnaces. This made cast iron possible, which, in turn, made possible even more versatile machinery.

A calculation by Leonardo

As the Renaissance unshackled men's minds, they began to sense the future significance of the machine. Envisioning bags of money that his projected needle-polishing machine might earn, Leonardo da Vinci wrote in his notebook: "Early tomorrow, Jan. 2, 1496, I shall . . . proceed to a trial. . . . One hundred times in each hour 400 needles will be finished, making 40,000 in an hour and 480,000 in 12 hours. Suppose we say 4,000 thousands which at 5 solidi per thousand gives 20,000 solidi: 1,000 lire per working day, and if one works 20 days in the month 60,000 ducats the year."

Toward the end of the 16th Century, William Lee, an English curate, developed a knitting machine that rattled out 1,000 to 1,500 stitches a minute, as against the 100 stitches that the fastest knitter could turn out by hand. A vocation that textile craftsmen had followed for generations was doomed. Both in England and on the Continent the first of countless and unequal human skirmishes began against the hated mechanical monsters. In 1596 an assassin hired by the Danzig city council strangled the inventor of a labor-saving ribbon loom. In 1753 English textile workers wrecked the home of John Kay, inventor of the flying shuttle, and forced him to flee the country. "Death to the engine!" cried a mob of Nottingham

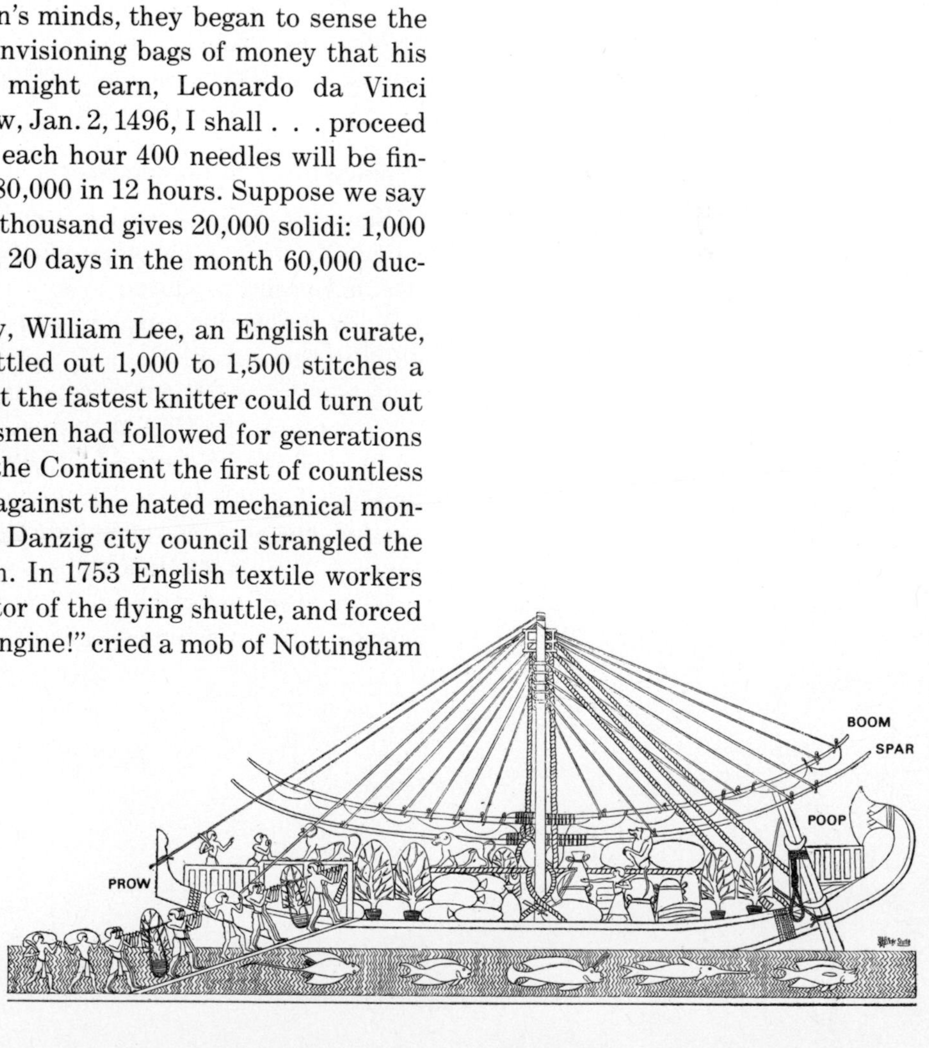

A SOPHISTICATED SEAFARER

The lure of rich cargoes beyond Egypt led to bigger, far more complex boats than the one opposite. Thirty oarsmen helped propel this vessel, which dates from 1500 B.C. Rigging allowed sails to be lowered, as shown at right, while ships lay at anchor. This was done by lowering the upper spar to the boom. Ropes from the mast to the spars helped to hoist the sail, while more rigging, leading to the prow and poop, supported the mast.

BOOM
SPAR
POOP
PROW

weavers called Luddites, as they smashed a textile-mill steam engine in 1815. (As recently as 1960, French automobile workers tried to destroy a computer that had selected the names of employees to be dropped from the payroll during a layoff period.)

From the start, it was a losing battle. Machines were proving too fast, too cheap to operate, too good at what they did. In a veritable torrent, men in England and Europe produced new inventions that could cut, bore, drill, grind, turn, polish, slit, shear, roll and stamp. Humans could not compete. When a plant built by Sir Samuel Bentham and Sir Marc Isambard Brunel to manufacture pulley blocks for the British Navy went into operation at Portsmouth in 1808, its bank of 44 different, steam-powered precision machines turned out blocks at the stupendous rate of 130,000 a year. Ten unskilled men, simply by tending the machines, did the work of 110 skilled blockmakers. Savings to the Admiralty, moreover, totaled a handsome £17,000 a year.

In America, confronting a continental wilderness to master, Yankee machines and machine-produced tools made the conquest possible: broadaxes that cleared the forests; James Oliver's chilled-iron plow that broke the tough sod of the prairies; Cyrus Hall McCormick's reaper, the weird, miraculous "cross between an Astley chariot, a wheelbarrow and a flying machine," as the London *Times* described it, that cut a 74-yard-long swath of wheat in 70 seconds; the "Yankee Geologist," a steam excavator that tore up a cubic yard of earth with one sweep of its iron claw, doing the job of 100 hearty pick-and-shovel men; Welcome Sprague's chain-fed corn cutter that sliced enough corn off the cob in a day to pack 15,000 cans; Scott and Chisholm's "pea-viner" that shelled peas all day long as fast as 600 humans working at top speed, and then was ready to keep going all night as well.

A slave army of horsepower

Since those high-spirited early days machine technology has boomed so swiftly and all-encompassingly that the 10,967,285,000-horsepower which America produced to run its machines in 1960 alone represented roughly the work-equivalent of 1,200 slaves for every man, woman and child in the nation. Machine population has long since outstripped human population. At our latest census in 1960, when there were 179,323,-000 people in the United States, there were 73,769,000 motor vehicles, 74,057,000 telephones, 55,500,000 television sets, 154,600,000 radios, and 574,178,000 electric clocks, coffee makers, mixers, ranges, shavers, vacuum cleaners, washers and other home appurtenances—a stupefying total of 932,104,000 machines.

Even more arresting in its way is our increased spending for automatic-control machines and automated manufacturing equipment, up from next to nothing in 1950 to $6.8 billion in 1961 to $8.4 billion in 1963. A particularly phenomenal rate of propagation characterizes the most redoubtable machine of all, the computer. The value of manufacturers' shipments of all computers rose from $350 million in 1950 (a minor fraction of this total was accounted for by cash registers) to $1.3 billion in 1960—an increase of more than 250 per cent. A dabbler in statistics has estimated that if the computer continues to proliferate at this pace, the entire surface of the earth by the year 2500 will be covered to a depth of at least six feet by computer-coded documents.

For all the predominance of the machine in our lives today, no modern assessment of its basic role has improved on the appraisal by Professor Reuleaux, back in 1875, in the *Kinematics of Machinery* cited previously ("kinematics" derives from the Greek *kinema*, or motion, and refers to the science of motion). Reuleaux, indeed, produced his opus because he was disturbed by the general lack of understanding of the machine, and so he determined to set down certain truths about it. He saw, first of all, that a machine imposes law and order on "the unrestrained power of natural forces, acting and reacting in limitless freedom." By its own built-in logic, it converts this power into refined, disciplined motion. The perfect machine is the perfection of discipline; its linkages are so interacting, and of such form and rigidity, that they permit each moving part one motion only—the required one. As a musician writing a score composes music, so an inventor designing a machine composes *motion*.

Two of the fundamentals propounded by Reuleaux reveal even to those who distrust and fear machines—and they are many—how irrevocably committed to them we humans are.

The first refers to the nature of the man-machine relationship. As Reuleaux saw it, most machines represent a closed kinematic chain—an interlinking of motions—that begins or ends with people. When we drive a car, the hand that turns the ignition key, the foot that depresses the accelerator pedal, the eyes that see the red light—all become essential parts of the machine, parts without which it could not function. We —our perceptions—are a vital link of the kinematic chain.

The poetic and geometric

The second Reuleaux fundamental refers to the geometry and, in a sense, to the poetry of the machine. Here he speaks of rotary motion— and touches a universal in our lives. We are a nation on wheels. The clocks that regulate our days and nights are crammed with wheels. Motion-picture reels spin; so do phonograph records, magnetic-tape reels, printing presses, gasoline-pump indicators, steamship propellers.

"Just as the old philosopher compared the constant gradual alteration of things to a flowing," wrote Reuleaux, "and condensed it into the

THE START OF A LOSING BATTLE
Among early foes of mechanization was a group of 19th Century English workmen called Luddites. In a fury against the textile machines that threw them out of jobs, they risked death penalties to wreck and set fire to mills. In this drawing, a Luddite leader, disguised as a woman, exhorts his followers to continue their rampage. Luddite riots broke out as late as the 1840s, even as craftsmen turned into docile tenders of the despised machines.

sentence: 'Everything flows;' so we may express the numberless motions in that wonderful production of the human brain which we call a machine in one word, 'Everything rolls'. . . . The same fundamental law of rolling applies to the mutual motions of the parts. . . . These . . . are as it were the soul of the machine, ruling its utterances—the bodily motions themselves—and giving them intelligible expression. They form the geometrical abstraction of the machine, and confer upon it, besides its outer meaning, an inner one, which gives it an intellectual interest to us far greater than any it could otherwise possess."

Man has put machines to shocking and tragic use. With them he has also achieved his proudest triumphs. But, strangely, when he is most intimately associated with a machine, when he knows and loves it best, it is not man who becomes machinelike; it is the machine that becomes manlike, singing and throbbing with living power. Charles Lindbergh, flying the Atlantic in 1927, sensed it. "The engine's even vibration, shaking back through the fuselage's steel skeleton, gives life to cockpit and controls," he wrote. "Flowing up along the stick to my hand, it's the pulse beat of the plane. Let a cylinder miss once, and I'll feel it as clearly as though a human heart had skipped against my thumb."

As for Lindbergh then, so for us now. Our destiny is unalterably bound up with the machine. There can be no turning back.

The Five Fundamental Machines

"Armed with his machinery man can dive, can fly, can see atoms like a gnat," said Ralph Waldo Emerson. "He can peer into Uranus with his telescope, or knock down cities with his fists of gunpowder." Today, we have machines that can do much more. Yet, the moving parts of all mechanical devices can still be reduced to combinations of the five "simple machines" known to the ancient Greeks—the lever, the wheel and axle, the pulley, the inclined plane and wedge, and the screw. The Greeks had also learned that a machine works because an "effort," which is exerted over an "effort distance," is magnified through "mechanical advantage" to overcome a "resistance" over a "resistance distance." Their discoveries are summarized in the modern formula: mechanical advantage = resistance ÷ effort, or = effort distance ÷ resistance distance. The five simplest applications of this formula are described in the following pages.

THE MASTERY OF LEVERAGE

Familiar examples of the five "simple machines" (opposite) are the lifting pulley, the oar (a lever), the potter's wheel (a wheel and axle), the air hammer (an inclined plane or wedge), the jack-screw and ship's propeller (both screws). The five simple machines of classic times are all related to each other, and it was long customary to refer them to a single natural principle: the law of the lever.

PULLEY

LEVER

WHEEL & AXLE

INCLINED PLANE AND WEDGE

SCREW

17

THE LEVER AS AN OAR

THE LEVER AS A HANDCAR HANDLE

THE LEVER AS A PUMP HANDLE

The Dillons

THE LEVER AS A CROWBAR

THE LEVER AS A SHOVEL

THE LEVER

Ancient Simple Levers:
Massive Power in Many Guises

THE LEVER AS A BATTER'S FOREARM

THE LEVER AS A WHEELBARROW

"How is it that dentists extract teeth more easily by applying . . . a tooth extractor than with the bare hand?" asked an ancient Greek theoretician. Archimedes gave the answer when he said that "equal weights at unequal distances . . . incline toward the weight which is at the greater distance." Both were talking about the oldest machine in the world: the lever.

Every lever has one fixed point called the "fulcrum" (in the case above, the pivot of the dentist's pliers), and is acted upon by two forces—the "effort" and the "weight" (dentist's muscle, tooth's resistance).

In its simplest form, the crowbar, the lever is a device that magnifies the effect of a small effort to move a large weight. But inverting the effort and the fulcrum changes the relationship; gripping a fishing pole and flipping a trout out of the water requires much more effort than the fish weighs. But the extra effort purchases the longer distance the fish travels.

A lever's guises are astonishingly numerous because the moving parts of any mechanical contrivance can be reduced to levers—in structure or in principle. Archimedes was neither immodest nor flippant when he said: "Give me a fulcrum on which to rest and I will move the earth."

WHY AND HOW A LEVER WORKS

Levers work according to a simple formula illustrated in the diagrams below: the effort multiplied by its distance from the fulcrum (effort arm) equals the weight multiplied by its distance from the fulcrum (weight arm). Thus, two pounds of effort exerted at a distance of four feet from the fulcrum will raise eight pounds located one foot from the fulcrum.

2 LBS.

4 FT. 1 FT. 8 LBS.

FULCRUM

THE THREE KINDS OF LEVERS

WEIGHT FULCRUM EFFORT

WEIGHT EFFORT FULCRUM

FULCRUM WEIGHT EFFORT

AN ASSORTMENT OF LEVERS

The three types of levers—conventionally called "first kind," "second kind" and "third kind"— are illustrated above by the pump handle *(left)*, the wheelbarrow *(right)* and the boxer's forearm *(center)*. Levers of the first kind have the fulcrum located between the effort and the weight. Examples are the oar, the crowbar, the weighing balance, a pair of scissors and a pair of pliers. Levers of the second kind—the handcar crank, doors—have the weight in the middle. Levers of the second kind magnify the effort. Levers of the third kind, such as a power shovel or a baseball batter's forearm, have the effort in the middle and always magnify the distance.

GEAR

TURBINE

WIND MILL

FERRIS WHEEL

THE WHEEL AND AXLE

From the Windlass to the
Steam Turbine: Levers in the Round

The ancients realized that the weight and effort in a lever were capable of describing a circle around its fulcrum. When they finally invented a lever that could rotate the full 360° of the circle, they had discovered the second of the five basic machines: the wheel and axle.

One of man's first uses for this elementary machine was in the windlass, to move a weight too heavy to be moved by hand. He tied a rope to the weight and then fastened the other end to an axle. Handspokes on the axle's wheel enabled him to turn it. Just as with a lever, the amount of exertion depends on the ratio of two lengths: that of the radius of the axle to the radius of the wheel. Thus, a 10-inch wheel on a one-inch axle magnifies force by 10. A 10-foot wheel on the same one-inch axle magnifies by 120. And just as levers can be operated by other levers, so the mechanical advantage of the wheel and axle can be stepped up by using a series of geared wheels of different sizes *(left)*. The remarkable versatility of these 360° levers is dramatically revealed in the various ways a wheel and axle are embodied in many familiar devices which we would never think of as wheels—a screwdriver, a water faucet, a key in a keyhole.

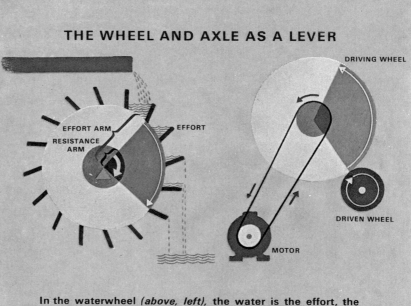

THE WHEEL AND AXLE AS A LEVER

DRIVING WHEEL

EFFORT ARM
RESISTANCE ARM

EFFORT

MOTOR

DRIVEN WHEEL

In the waterwheel *(above, left)*, the water is the effort, the wheel's radius is the effort arm, the force the millstone exerts on the axle is the resistance and the axle's radius is the resistance arm. The second diagram shows a motor *(above, right)* turning a large wheel which turns a small one. As the larger turns 120° *(shaded area)*, the smaller completes a whole turn. The large wheel's speed of rotation is magnified three times.

A ROUNDUP OF WHEELS

The waterwheel, windmill and turbine *(painting at left)* all convert the kinetic energy of a moving substance (water, air, steam) to the mechanical energy of a rotating axle. The potter's wheel may have been the first wheel that man used. Some of the wheels shown here are passive rollers—that is, they merely roll instead of being wheel-and-axle "circular levers." Examples: the skate's rollers, the bicycle's rear wheel, the roller belt's small wheels, and all the train's wheels except the locomotive's four large drivers (which are moved by connecting rods as the bicycle's driver is by pedal cranks). The roller belt is driven by its larger toothed wheels.

WINDLASS AND PULLEY

DRIVE PULLEYS

LIFTING PULLEY

ROMAN CRANE

FIXED PULLEY

TWO-SHEAVED BLOCK

THE PULLEY

From Bucket Lift
to Electric Construction Hoist

"If we want to move any weight whatever, we tie a rope to this weight and . . . pull the rope until we lift it. And for this is needed a power equal to the weight that we want to lift. But if we untie the rope from the weight, and tie one of its ends to a solid crossbeam and pass its other end [around] a pulley fastened to the middle of the burden and draw on the rope, our moving of that weight will be easier."

This Third Century account is one of the oldest and clearest descriptions of the difference between a fixed pulley *(below, left)* and a movable pulley *(below,*

center). The fixed pulley gives the puller no aid. For any more complex system of pulleys threaded by only a single rope, the mechanical advantage is given by the number of rope segments that support the weight. Such advantage, however, is achieved at some cost; a smaller effort is required to lift a weight, but the distance through which the effort must move increases in direct proportion to the mechanical advantage obtained. Thus, using the block and tackle *(below, right)* to raise the 60-pound weight three feet *(black bar)* requires 20 pounds of effort to be exerted through a distance of nine feet *(red bar)*.

FUNICULAR HOIST

BLOCK

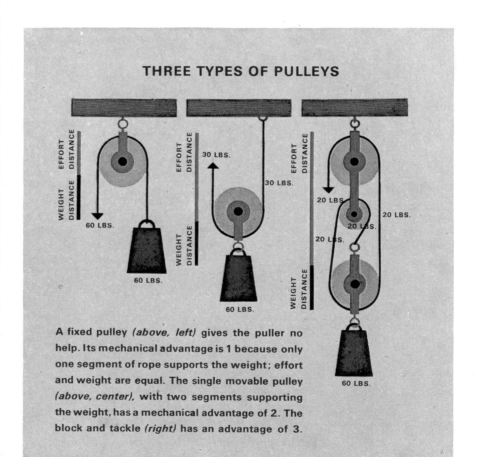

THREE TYPES OF PULLEYS

A fixed pulley *(above, left)* gives the puller no help. Its mechanical advantage is 1 because only one segment of rope supports the weight; effort and weight are equal. The single movable pulley *(above, center)*, with two segments supporting the weight, has a mechanical advantage of 2. The block and tackle *(right)* has an advantage of 3.

A CLUTCH OF PULLEYS

The windlass and pulley for drawing water from a well *(painting, opposite)* comprise one of the oldest uses of the simple fixed pulley. The Romans improved on this primitive crane by replacing the windlass with a treadmill. The block and tackle uses multiple pulleys, as exemplified by the two-sheaved block dominating the paint-

ing. Other details show a block with an eye for a hook; three drive pulleys of different sizes interconnected with flexible belts so that they change each other's rotational speeds; a fixed pulley; a complex block and tackle in the form of a funicular hoist; and a simple lifting pulley of the kind shown in the center diagram above.

A CARPENTER'S PLANE

A HAND CHISEL

A SPLITTING WEDGE

AN AIR HAMMER

A GANGPLOW

A HATCHET

AN INCLINED PLANE

THE INCLINED PLANE AND WEDGE

A "V" That Meant Victory in Easing Human Labor

Ramps, sloping roads, chisels, hatchets, plows, air hammers, carpenters' planes—all these are examples of the fourth basic machine: the inclined plane and its active twin brother, the wedge. In the broadest sense, the wedge includes all devices for cutting and piercing—everything from a kitchen knife to the "flying wedge" of football, a play so effective in splitting the opponents' formation it was outlawed.

It is easier to understand how a wedge works by looking at the inclined plane, which is nothing more than a wedge sliced in half (*diagrams below*). While the wedge does its job by moving, the inclined plane is held stationary while the "wedged material" is moved over it. The secret of the plane's mechanical advantage: for an object resting on the plane, the vertical force of gravity acting on it is split into two smaller forces, one perpendicular to, one parallel to the plane. And it is only the parallel force which needs to be counteracted by pushing. If there is no friction on the plane, the pushing effort required will be one tenth the weight if the length of the plane is 10 times its height. A similar relationship holds for any plane; the extra distance makes it possible to apply an effort smaller than the weight.

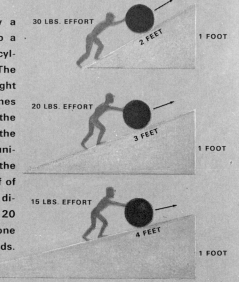

THE MATHEMATICS OF AN INCLINED PLANE

The diagrams *(right)* show a man pushing a cylinder up a smooth inclined plane. The cylinder weighs 60 pounds. The ratio of the triangle's height to its hypotenuse determines how much effort *(arrows)* the man must exert to move the cylinder up the plane at a uniform speed. Top diagram: the answer is obviously one half of 60, or 30 pounds. Middle diagram: one third of 60, or 20 pounds. Bottom diagram: one quarter of 60, or 15 pounds.

30 LBS. EFFORT — 2 FEET — 1 FOOT

20 LBS. EFFORT — 3 FEET — 1 FOOT

15 LBS. EFFORT — 4 FEET — 1 FOOT

WITH AN INCLINED PLANE—JUST AS WITH A LEVER, PULLEY OR WHEEL AND AXLE—ANY DECREASE IN FORCE IS ACCOMPANIED BY A RECIPROCAL INCREASE IN THE DISTANCE.

A MONTAGE OF WEDGES

In the montage at left, there are six different varieties of wedges—a chisel, a hatchet, a gangplow, an air hammer, a carpenter's plane and a splitting wedge. Because of its layered structure, wood can be easily split or shaped by wedges; thus carpenters and woodcutters were among the first to use this simple machine in making the tools of their trade. The plow, which is actually several wedges, does not so much break the soil as turn it. The ramp with a barrel being pushed up it is an inclined plane, the machine from which the wedge is derived. The ramp in the painting is having its efficiency impaired by the wedge at the end of the air hammer.

AN EYE SCREW

A SCREW HOOK

A CARPENTER'S CLAMP

AN EYEBOLT

CALIPERS

A VISE

AN OLD PAPER PRESS

A CORKSCREW

A ROUNDHEAD SCREW

A BOLT AND NUT

A WORM GEAR

A BRACE AND BIT

A METAL SCREW

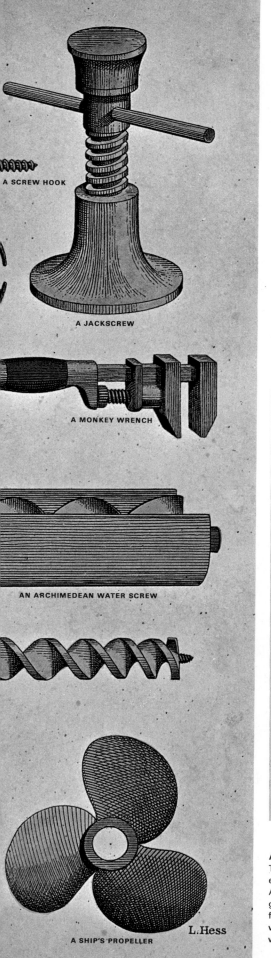

A SCREW HOOK

A JACKSCREW

A MONKEY WRENCH

AN ARCHIMEDEAN WATER SCREW

A SHIP'S PROPELLER

L.Hess

THE SCREW

Complexity in Simplicity:
A New Twist for the Wedge

Around 200 B.C., a Greek mathematician, Apollonius of Perga, worked out the geometry of the spiral helix, and laid the groundwork for the fifth and youngest of the simple machines: the screw.

In one sense, a screw is not a "simple" machine at all since it depends upon another machine, a lever, for its operation. It can be looked at as a twisted wedge that derives its power not from percussion but from being turned by a lever *(diagrams below)*. Put in a different way, it can be imagined as a cylinder with an inclined plane wrapped around it *(below, left)*. The most famous screws of antiquity

were those of Archimedes: one of them was designed to raise water *(left)*, another enabled him to drag a fully loaded three-masted ship onto dry land.

The screw can function in two principal ways: it can raise weights and it can press or fasten objects. In the former role, it converts rotary motion into straight-line motion. It was first used as a fastener by ancient goldsmiths for locking bracelets. A screw finds its mechanical advantage in the ratio of two dimensions: the length of the lever that turns it and the distance between threads (or pitch), as shown in the diagram below, right.

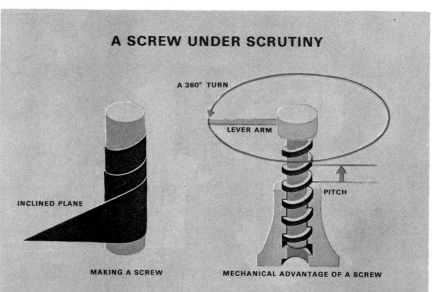

A SCREW UNDER SCRUTINY

A 360° TURN

LEVER ARM

INCLINED PLANE

PITCH

MAKING A SCREW

MECHANICAL ADVANTAGE OF A SCREW

The principle of the screw can be easily understood by cutting a right triangle out of paper and wrapping it around a pencil *(above, left)*. The triangle's hypotenuse becomes the inclined plane, or threads, of the screw. The right-hand diagram shows that when the lever arm makes a full turn in the direction of the arrow, the screw is elevated a distance equal to the pitch, or the gap between adjacent threads.

A MISCELLANY OF SCREWS

The old press *(opposite)* was used to squeeze excess sizing out of paper. A modern version of Archimedes' famous water screw is the meat grinder. In the ship's propeller, the three screw-form blades act like oars, thrusting against the water behind them; they are also drawn forward by the lower pressure ahead of them. The

calipers are actually a lever of the third kind in which the screw and wing nut supply the effort. A screw and nut are opposed twins. The hollow nut is an inversion of the solid screw in that the spiral helix is cut into the inner surface of a cylindrical cavity rather than raised in relief on the external surface of a solid cylinder.

2

A Seasoned
Instrument for
War or Peace

WHEEL OF BENEFICENCE
Along with contrivances far less amiable, men of ancient times devised machines to help them live a better life. Outstanding among these was a wheel to harness the power of flowing water for irrigation purposes. Although largely replaced as a power source by steam engines, waterwheels such as the one above, shown gracing a Cambodian landscape, still flourish.

THREE THINGS, without which man could not live, inspired the machines of classic times: war, diversion and work. Several thousand years of experience and today's more sophisticated semantics have refined the categories to two: machines are either positive, devoted to human welfare and life, or negative, dedicated to human destruction and death. There are, on the one hand, the myriad contrivances that lighten labor, invite leisure and allay pain. There are, on the other hand, missiles, rockets, flamethrowers, the B-52, the Polaris, the computers programmed to calculate megadeaths (millions killed) and "bonus kills" (deaths from fallout) in the event of attack, and the H-bomb itself, the doomsday machine, whose sheer hideousness may ironically make it a mechanical friend to man after all: the one that appalls him into peace.

The same ceaseless counterpoint between the ways of peace and the ways of war characterized man's machines in centuries past. Only the magnitude has changed.

Hot or cold, war has always been a prolific machine breeder. In the Seventh Century B.C., Assyrian armies were assaulting the ramparts of hostile cities with monster battering rams mounted on wheels; some, called "tortoises," were plated with an armor of stiff green hide for protection from arrow-fire. A few hundred years later, the Greek generals Alexander and Demetrius were building wheeled towers, 10 to 20 levels high, with drawbridges at the various levels across which their attacking forces could storm to hand-to-hand combat on enemy battlements; a basic machine element, pulleys with ropes—block and tackle—made it possible to haul these huge structures to strategic positions alongside the walls. Another punishing device is attributed to that bright star of Greek science, Archimedes: a huge iron claw which, during a Roman siege of his native Syracuse, lifted whole vessels of the invading fleet and dashed them on the rocks.

Other Greek triumphs included massive and primitive engines of death driven by torsion power—the same power you see if you stretch a rubber band between thumb and forefinger, wind a pencil stub between its two lengths, then let go. Both the *euthytonon*, a dart-hurling catapult, and the *palintonon*, a rock thrower, featured twin skeins of tightly twisted cords, sinew or human hair. Long wooden arms were inserted through the skeins, then pulled back by ropes attached to windlasses much like oversized fishing reels. These were equipped with ratchets—a series of notches into which fitted a pivoted catch. When released, the arms whipped forward with annihilating force and flung an iron-tipped spear or 10-pound stone at the hapless target.

Some of the same fertile minds which produced the lethal weapons of the Hellenistic world also devised its instruments of peace. Archimedes, for example, is believed to have invented the water-raising cochlea, or screw (*shown on page 31*) with simple but highly effective convolutions. In modified form, it is used for irrigation to this day in the Mediterranean back country. Another water raiser—the force pump—is credited to a contemporary of Archimedes, Ctesibius. This was almost certainly the first application of today's familiar piston-cylinder mechanism, whose workings can be illustrated by a hypodermic syringe, its glass tube representing the cylinder, its plunger the piston. Two cylinders with pistons were worked by means of rods and handles. The intake stroke sucked water through a valve into the base of one cylinder; pressure on the exhaust stroke closed the valve, and at the same time drove the water out of the cylinder through a pipe.

Feats of a gadgeteer

An equally basic principle of modern machinery appeared in a gadget devised by Hero of Alexandria. In pursuit of a favorite hobby—constructing mechanical conveniences for temple and theater—Hero put together an *anemourion,* a wind machine for powering a small organ. Its key feature was a cam—a short, rigid stick protruding from the axle of a wheel fitted with wind scoops. As the wind turned the wheel, the cam depressed a lever which raised the piston which provided air for the organ; as the cam continued on around, slipping past the lever, the piston fell back. By converting rotary motion into up-and-down reciprocating motion, the wheel and cammed axle proved yet another primary machine element.

But Hero's most remarkable device was the *aeolipile.* A toy, put to no known practical use, it consisted of no more than a small, water-filled copper pot on a tripod, yet it was the progenitor of the modern steam turbine. Through two holes in the pot lid ran two tubes—one hollow—angled in so that between them they supported a hollow globe free to rotate on a horizontal axis. Two little pipes protruded from the globe, bent back at right angles, like the arms of a swastika. To make the *aeolipile* whirl, a fire was lighted under the vessel. When the water boiled, steam rose through the hollow tube into the globe and came shooting and spitting out of the bent pipes. Its jetlike burst set the globe spinning merrily.

What these gifted Greek mechanicians did, they did with flair and elegance; but it remained for a pragmatic Roman engineer of the First Century B.C.—sloshing around, perhaps, in the Pontine drainage ditches—to put machines to serious, heavy work. He accomplished this in one simple, inspired stroke: he turned the crude Norse wheel on edge and thus invented a basic prime mover, the vertical waterwheel. The new wheel, called the Vitruvian because it was first described by the architect Vitruvius, was apparently undershot, that is, driven by a stream

A MEDIEVAL SCOURGE OF BATTLE

The dragon-shaped "attack tower" above appears in a 15th Century Italian treatise on weaponry. Seemingly a figment of fantasy, this mechanical monster had counterparts in real life. Such contraptions were moved on rollers to enemy walls; often arrow-shaped missiles were shot from cannons in their mouths. They were purposely made to look grotesque so as to inspire dread in the foe.

A ROMAN COLOSSUS AT WORK

The Romans' flair for doing things in a big way is seen in this side-view reconstruction of the flour mills they built at Barbegal, France, to exploit waterpower on an unprecedented scale. The mechanism consisted of two sets of eight wheels stepped down a hillside. Sheds between the wheels housed 16 sets of millstones, each powered by its own wheel.

flowing beneath it. Eventually three types of waterwheel were in operation: the undershot variety, the breast wheel and, most efficient of all, the great overshot wheel *(illustrated on page 32)*.

The Vitruvian wheel came into use at a propitious time in the affairs of Rome. Militarily, the Empire was losing its thrust. Slavery was on the wane; no longer were vast gangs available for endless tramping on treadmills. The populace was clamoring for cheaper bread. To fill the need, engineers soon were constructing machines almost as monumental as the Colosseum itself; for example, the Barbegal flour mills *(sketched below, left)*, built near Arles about the Fourth Century, are said to have produced 28 tons of flour in one 10-hour day, enough for 80,000 people.

As time passed, man found new ways to extend his groping mechanical knowledge. Curiously, the torpor which settled over culture and learning during the Dark Ages did not apply to technology. The need for weapons and tools kept men improving old machines and devising new ones even during that sunless era. The development of the iron horseshoe and practical pulling harness rendered the horse an effective prime mover in about the 10th Century; powerful mills utilizing the wind reached from England to Russia by the 13th Century.

But it was water—and the waterwheel—that continued to be man's single greatest source of power until the coming of steam. Water was storable, required no oats or stable space, never grew ill, old or tired, and—unlike the wind—was seldom if ever fickle. It tumbled down from the mountains ever eager to spin the big wheels for the revenue of the manor, the profit of the miller, the betterment of the lot of everyman. As waterwheels were improved, they powered machinery that sawed wood, pressed olives and processed cloth. Even more exciting, water power could be harnessed for the rich gold, silver, copper, iron, zinc and lead mines along the swift streams of Central Europe.

Bustle, blast and heave-ho

Medieval drawings of scenes deep in the Black Forest of Germany depict the bustle of the new mechanization—puffing bellows, flaring blast furnaces, clanging anvils, clattering drop hammers, pounding ore crushers, gnomelike little men heave-hoing on ropes and chains. These operations marked a portentous advance in machine evolution: the conversion of the waterwheel's rotary motion into the reciprocating motion essential to mining and metallurgical processes.

The key in most conversion mechanisms proved to be the cams originated by Hero of Alexandria. An ore crusher, for example, consisted of a waterwheel whose main axle was fitted with two, perhaps three, protruding cams. As they revolved, they successively struck, from beneath, a peg attached to an upright shaft. Fitted to the lower end of the shaft was a

MONUMENT TO A GREEK GENIUS
Attributed to Archimedes, this water-raising screw, shown in cross section, had a technological impact out of all proportion to its simplicity. Widely used for irrigation, it consisted of a round wooden beam wrapped spirally with strips of wood on edge, then encased in boards. Angled into the water and spun by foot, it caused the water to climb the spiral and gush out.

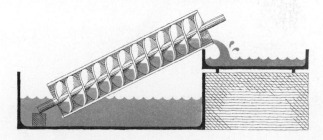

heavy metal hammer. Thus each cam, in passing, lifted the shaft-and-hammer, then let it drop with pulverizing force on the ore below. Sometimes, however, the weight of the hammer—or of other tools in other processes—was not enough to complete the cycle. To solve the problem, clever tinkerers rigged up a resilient overhead pole. As depicted in a 13th Century French drawing of a machine saw in operation, waterpowered cam action against a frame which held the lower end of the saw blade drove the saw down against the pull of a light spring-pole fixed to the blade's upper end. As the cams released the frame, the pole straightened, snapping the saw into the upstroke.

This spring-pole innovation built into a machine a responsiveness never before realized. It soon found enormously significant application in the lathe, the device that spins a workpiece of wood, metal or other material while a cutting or shaping tool is applied to its revolving surface. It is one of the most enduring of man's mechanical helpmeets; archeologists have found wooden bowls, obviously "turned" on a lathe, dating back to the Second Century B.C. Today lathes are among the most basic of all machine tools: "machines that make machines," that cut screws, crankshafts and other vital metal machine parts to the incredible, ten-thousandth-of-an-inch tolerances required by modern mass production. The way for all this was cleared when turners in the 12th Century church and monastery workshops of France and Germany adapted the spring-pole mechanism to their lathes and connected it to foot treadles. The mechanical linkage of treadle-and-pole enabled the turner for the first time to rotate the workpiece himself, and coordinate its action more precisely with that of the cutting tool.

A new role for the crank

The vastly underrated technology of the Middle Ages also wrought a momentous change in the fundamental machine element we all know as the crank—first depicted in the Ninth Century Utrecht Psalter as a means of turning a grindstone. Engineers faced the problem of using a crank to convert rotary motion of windmill or waterwheel into a continuous, power-driven reciprocating cycle that would, say, operate a pump or drive a piston in a cylinder all day long. Oddly, it may have been the carpenter's brace—the hand tool used even today for boring holes—that inspired the solution. Someone squared the curve of the brace, looped the end of a rod around it, and thus invented a key element of the automobile, of powered flight and a dozen other modern machine functions of nearly equal stature: the crank-and-connecting rod.

But even as such devices relieved medieval man of enervating drudgery, machines with less hopeful implications appeared. One was the cannon, a one-cylinder internal-combustion engine, the most concen-

THREE WHEELS AND THREE WAYS TO EXPLOIT THE FLOW OF WATER

THE UNDERSHOT WHEEL
Water coursing beneath this wheel, hitting its lower paddles, is what causes it to rotate. It is the stream's direction *(dark arrows)* that makes the wheel turn counterclockwise.

THE BREAST WHEEL
A wheel placed to catch falling water at midway point can be equipped with buckets on its paddles. The weight of the water caught by the buckets speeds the rotation of the wheel.

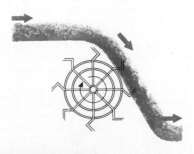

THE OVERSHOT WHEEL
Water falling on a wheel from above also allows the use of buckets on the paddles. Both overshot and breast wheels gain added speed from the force of the falling water.

trated mechanism of destruction yet created, and forerunner of whole generations of weapons both larger and smaller and invariably more deadly: bombard siege guns, multifiring ribaudequins, the matchlock musket, the flintlock muzzle-loader, the wheel lock cavalry pistol.

Cannon came on the European scene, it is believed, in the early 1300s, not long after the introduction of black Chinese gunpowder. The first models were hand-fashioned. Villainously small and chunky, weighing some 40 pounds or less, they spread rapidly. Edward III of England cannonaded Calais when he besieged the city in 1346. The armaments industry began its swift ascent. Within a century, gunmakers were building huge 400- and 600-pound cannon from long, forged iron bars; they welded the bars together lengthwise around a core, reinforced them with iron hoops, then removed the core and blocked one end.

Exit the lance and the lily

Firearms gave warfare a grim new impersonal touch. It was one thing to watch a 60-pound stone come lobbing lazily over the castle walls from a swaying trebuchet—the missile hurler of its day—across the moat; it was quite another thing to feel the earth tremble, hear the roar of distant cast-iron or bronze bombards, then see them pound your supposedly indestructible wall to pieces. Earlier battles had often been chivalrous skirmishes of lances on lily-strewn fields of honor. Now armies sought each other's total destruction and even attacked urban populations.

Far-reaching as the effects of such weaponry were to be, two more inventions of the Middle Ages were to have no less profound an impact on humanity everywhere: the mechanical clock and the printing press.

The development of clock mechanisms begot priceless practical knowledge of small geared or toothed wheels—how to mesh them together, how to control a falling weight, how to regulate the recoil of a delicate spring. It was this competence, laboriously gained, that made possible such notable scientific accomplishments as the pendulum studies of Galileo and Huygens, marine chronometers for determining longitude, all manner of precision instruments. But the mechanical clock struck haunting personal overtones as well. Inescapably booming out each fleeting hour, it prodded man to bestir himself and get on with the work of the world—giving him a sense of urgency less likely to be aroused by sandglass or sundial.

Who invented the mechanical clock, when or where, is not known. But the development of its basic principle, in the light of contemporary knowledge, was a work of unparalleled brilliance. The inventor's reasoning might have gone something like this: if I attach a weight to a rope, and pass the rope a number of times around a short cylinder or barrel that is free to revolve; if I elevate this mechanism on a framework or

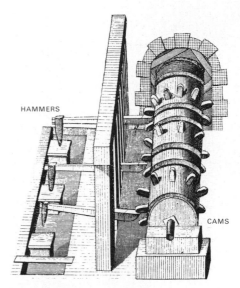

HAMMERS

CAMS

A CASE OF MOTIVE POWER

As depicted in the 18th Century encyclopedia of the French philosopher Denis Diderot, the foundry apparatus above incorporated a basic machine element dating back to the Greeks: the wheel and cammed axle. As the axle *(right)* was turned by a waterwheel *(beyond hole in wall)*, it rotated. Its cams, or protruding knobs, hit the hammer handles *(left)*, thus converting the wheel's rotary motion into the hammers' up-and-down motion.

tower, and regulate the fall of the weight so that it slowly drops a certain distance toward the ground between sunrise and sunset, unwinding the rope and turning the barrel as it drops; if I manage all this, then, by means of a toothed wheel on the end of the barrel, and other wheels geared to it, the movement of the weight could be registered by a convenient indicator, moving correspondingly around the face of a dial through the hours of a day. I could then rewind the rope on the barrel, thus raising the weight, and repeat the process the next day.

Triumph in a chapel tower

History's first reliable reference to a mechanical clock is to one built in the chapel tower of the Visconti Palace in Milan in 1335. Possibly 30 more were built during the next 35 years. All were great public clocks whose gears were arduously hand-filed; all were weight-driven. The problem of constraining the fall of a dropping weight was first solved by an ingenious device known as the verge escapement. A key component was the serrated, or saw-toothed, "crown" wheel, so called from its somewhat remote resemblance to a king's crown; it was driven by a series of wheels turned by the pull of the weight. Across the crown wheel's axis extended a metal bar known as a verge, from the Latin *virga*, or rod. Fastened at either end of the verge, where it touched the wheel's perimeter at the top or bottom, were two small metal plates, or "pallets." As the crown wheel turned, the verge moved back and forth, its pallets engaging, then releasing, a sawtooth at a time on opposite sides of the wheel, thereby allowing them to "escape." The speed of the wheel's advance—thus the weight's fall—was regulated by a weighted balance arm called a "foliot," swinging to and fro above the verge.

In spite of their crudities, such early clocks were heroic machines, sculpture in metal, embodying a revolution in ideas and concepts: the mechanical constraint of motion; machine measurement of the flow of time; revelations of a new environmental dimension and, most significant, the bold imposition of man-conceived order upon it.

As with the mechanical clock, the invention of printing cannot be credited to one man, one country, one year. It was an astounding composite of hard-won and far-flung triumphs: the manufacture of paper, begun in First Century China; the development of oil-based ink, delayed until experiments of 15th Century Flemish artists with boiled linseed oil as a paint base and varnish; the knowledge gained from printing with carved wooden blocks, used in medieval Europe to produce religious prints and playing cards; the concept of metal type, individually cast in molds, first put into effect in Korea in the late 14th Century; the craft, developed by German goldsmiths, of cutting hard steel or brass punches that would leave the impression of a letter of the alphabet if hammered

A CLOCK "ANYONE" COULD BUILD

These are the motion works of an ingenious 14th Century clock which took 16 years to build. It could record the movements of celestial bodies as well as tick off the hours. Its maker was a Florentine physician, Giovanni Dondi, who published the details of its construction and loftily asserted that "if the student of the MS cannot complete this clock for himself, he is wasting his time in studying the MS further."

against a softer metal; the adaptation of the screw press, familiar to Hero in antiquity, and presently used to press linen and grapes.

In the studios of Rhineland artisans, in the wood-block print shops of Haarlem and Mainz, men little by little assembled the materials and skills that suddenly, in the 1440s, reached a kind of flash point that fused them into the most powerful machines ever devised. There are those who have ranked the invention of the printing press with man's discovery of fire. Indeed, it was and is a machine that sets fires in the minds and hearts of men. "With my twenty-six metal soldiers," boasted an early French printer, "I have conquered the world."

The event commonly accepted as the start of organized printing occurred one day in a Rhineland print shop not later than 1448, when a simple hand press produced on paper from movable type a poem called *World Judgement* and an astronomical calendar. It is known that one man, Johann Gutenberg, was involved in this operation, possibly with two others, Johann Fust and Fust's son-in-law, Peter Schoeffer.

The Gutenberg triumph signaled the start of other fateful things. One was mass production. About 1400, an Italian nobleman had hired 45 scriveners to hand-copy a host of manuscripts for his private library. In two laborious years they produced 200 volumes. Half a century later a single skilled printer in Gutenberg's shop could turn out 300 pages in one day. Coming off the press one after another, printed pages were the first standardized, serially produced items turned out by man. Movable-type characters, moreover, represented still another original feature of mass-production technology: standardized, re-usable parts.

Men everywhere had been hungering for the exchange of ideas, for the space-defying, mind-to-mind communication that printing, in one Promethean stroke, made possible. By 1500, plants in 14 European countries had produced upward of eight million books. In another hundred years or so, printing presses were in the New World.

Visions of a perfectionist

But the transcendent achievement of the Middle Ages was the mind of one man: Leonardo da Vinci. He who painted perfection in *The Last Supper* showed just as radiant genius in his mechanical drawings. Many of his concepts in hydraulics, anatomy, optics, physics, and military arms and engineering were generations ahead of his time. In the design of machines of all kinds and in the delineation of machine principles, he stood alone and peerless.

Their range was stupendous:
• An armored car powered from within by man-turned cranks.
• A *clotonbrot*, first modern gas shell, a projectile packed with gunpowder, sulphur, and iron balls. "The most lethal machine that exists,"

A CLOCK FIT FOR A KING

This intricate Oriental water clock was built for a 13th Century sultan, Nâsir ad-Dîn Mahmûd. Every half hour, the bird *(top)* would whistle and the elephant driver would beat a tattoo with his drumstick. Simultaneously, the man in the window would make the falcon release a pellet. This made the dragon writhe before it hit a gong inside the elephant and fell into a bowl. The sultan could tot up the passing hours by counting the fallen pellets.

he noted. "The center ball bursts and scatters the rest, which it sets on fire, within a period no longer than an Ave Maria."

• A flying machine made of wood or reed and cloth, with graceful bat-wings that the pilot would manipulate with cranks or springs. It would, Leonardo predicted, soar aloft on its maiden flight from Mount Ceceri, near Fiesole, "bringing eternal glory to its birthplace."

• An alarm clock that roused the sleeper by a lever that tilted his feet —"for the use of those who watch jealously over the use of their time."

• A diving suit that would enable a man to stay under water for four hours. Mechanical diggers for excavating canals. Ratchet, wheel and gearing mechanisms to convert reciprocating into rotary motion. A power loom ". . . second only to the printing press in importance," Leonardo wrote; ". . . a lucrative, beautiful and subtle invention."

Of the multitudinous notes and drawings that he left behind, many represent reports of the work of others. Of those that are pure Leonardo, many are unfinished fragments, and never materialized in machinery in his time. Even so, they are an inspiring legacy, for this matchless man brought something new into the world: imagination in engineering and invention. He glimpsed future miracles, wondrous machines to come, comprehending them from afar, and now the future he envisioned is our present, this day in which we live.

Weapons from Slingshots to Gunpowder

Throughout his history man has used increasingly complex machines to fight his battles. Some time about the 10th Century B.C. ". . . David put his hand in his bag, and took thence a stone, and slang it, and smote the Philistine. . . ." Thus, in I Samuel 17:49, is chronicled one of the best-known early uses of a machine to kill a man. David used leverage to flatten the giant Goliath; the sling lengthened David's arm—or lever—and this extra length gave his stone extra momentum. Combat machines give the man or army using them an advantage. But soon the enemy has the machines too. So the search for new machines goes on. In the fourth millennium B.C. some unknown inventor mounted crude wheels beneath a platform (opposite) and the field of combat was changed forever. The wedge, the ram, torsion and tension all became parts of efficient war machines that ruled the battlefield for centuries—until at last gunpowder took over.

AN ANCIENT MISSILE CARRIER
A spear thrower of Ur, a Sumerian city north of the Persian Gulf, rides to battle with his driver in a four-wheeled chariot pulled by asses. Each wooden wheel consists of two semicircular disks doweled together against the hub. In the upper panel, spear-carrying infantrymen march to battle wearing protective helmets of copper and ankle-length cloaks probably made of heavy felt.

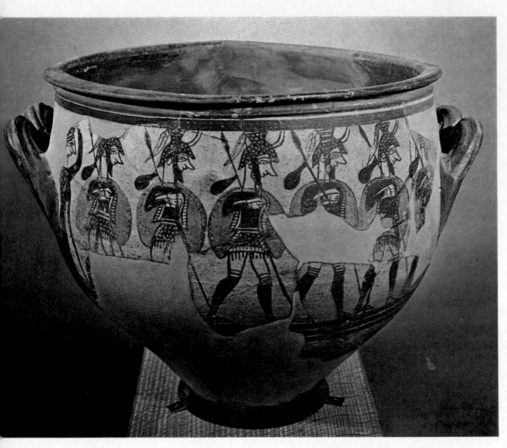

Wedge and Lever: A Murderous Team for Battle

The principles of the wedge and lever applied to machines of battle produced a fearsome group of weapons. In the beginning, Stone Age man fought with ax and spear. By chipping away at stone, these primitive warriors produced the hand ax, a kind of wedge. When they attached it to a handle they coupled the wedge's advantage to that of the lever. Similarly, primitive man's spears utilized the human arm as a lever to propel the wedge—the spear itself. Thousands of years later—about 3000 B.C.—man invented bronze and found that his new metal could be honed from a blunt splitting wedge into an extremely sharp cutting sword. Again, in use the sword linked the advantage of the lever—arm and sword itself—with that of the wedge—the cutting edge.

From stone to bronze to iron weapons, the basic principles were the same but ingenuity contributed endless refinements. The efficient Viking ax, with a cutting edge often as long as 12 inches, was a prototype of the poleax, a weapon soon adapted and modified by every fighting force in Europe (lower left).

All these wedge-lever combinations for war were personal weapons—used by one individual against another individual. And their development sparked the development of personal armor. From the days of earliest Greece (upper left) on through the days of knighthood in the Middle Ages (opposite) warriors carried burdensome loads into battle. Armed and mounted, a knight was an awesomely powerful machine: more than a ton of man, armor and horse hurtling at the foe.

A PHALANX OF DEADLY SPEARS

Spear-carrying early Greek infantrymen advance to battle in this scene on a Mycenaean warrior vase. These spear carriers defended a civilization which flourished between 1600 and 1100 B.C. Long before Grecian times, the spear—a slender pole with a fire-hardened tip, later refined with stone or metal points—was used by primitive peoples for war and hunting.

WEAPONS TO EXTEND THE ARM

In the first test of the halberd (below right), the Swiss proved in 1315 at the battle of Morgarten that not even knights of Austria could stand against it. For centuries weapons similar to the 15th Century quartet below were wielded with deadly effect. In the last European battle won by axes the Marquis of Montrose defeated the Covenanters at Tippermuir in Scotland in 1644.

POLEAX
BURGUNDIAN

BEC DE CORBIN
ITALIAN

WAR HAMMER
FRENCH

HALBERD
SWISS

A CLASH OF MOUNTED POWER

Jousting knights meet on collision courses in the British Museum's heraldic manuscript entitled "The Military Roll," compiled about 1480. When the first spear-carrying nobleman clambered astride his mount, he unwittingly brought immense additional power to his weapon: the extra weight and speed of the horse probably increased his lance's efficiency by 10 times.

The Battering Ram: A New Machine to Flatten Cities

Early in man's history he erected walls around settlements to protect himself from marauders. Almost as soon as they were raised, the walls were breached. Attackers tunneled under and climbed over.

Two of the most effective machines for breaking through a defensive wall were the battering ram and the bore. A ram was simply a huge tree trunk tipped with a blunt blob of metal; carried by men or swung on ropes like a pendulum, the ram crashed repeatedly into masonry walls until they crumbled. The bore, a similar device with a pointed, metal-covered tip, probed weak spots in the masonry joints.

The ram was often incorporated into another terrifying machine, the tower. Built from timbers on the site of a siege, this huge device often reached a height of 20 stories. (The First Century Roman engineer-architect Vitruvius described the small towers as 90 feet high, large ones as twice that.) Within their armored walls of board and animal hides, the towers contained many levels with connecting ladders, drawbridges, a massive battering ram in the base, and a crew of archers and rock-throwing soldiers at the pinnacle.

NAKED POWER ON FOOT

Dacian tribesmen batter a Roman position in this scene from Trajan's column, about 110 A.D. Their ram, decorated with a metal ram's-head tip, is an anachronism. The hand-carried ram had long been superseded by rope-slung rams which were more efficient machines of battle.

DEVASTATION ON WHEELS

An Assyrian fighting tower, its projecting ram battering the enemy's wall, forces a surrender from the defending chieftain (figure atop wall with hand upraised). The attacking king *(far left)* shoots from a protected position behind the tower. This relief is from the Ninth Century B.C.

Power in Storage for Heavy Artillery's Engines of War

About 400 B.C. the Greeks put the forces of torsion and tension to work in war machines. It was not for some 1,500 years that yet another simple source of power—counterpoise—was exploited. (Torsion is the twisting force of the rubber band that powers a model airplane; tension is the force of the same rubber band propelling a spitball. Counterpoise is a father's foot balancing a child on a seesaw.) The war machines that used these forces were devices for creating and storing power to be released in a surge.

In torsion machines such as the onager (*below*), the lever was pulled back against the force of tightly twisted rope, sinew or hair. When released, the lever could fling 50-pound rocks a distance of 400 yards.

Torsion and tension artillery was supreme until the 12th Century invention of the counterpoise-powered trebuchet (*left*).

The onager kicked back when discharged.

FANCIFUL USE FOR COUNTERPOISE
A Biblical artilleryman draws down the sling of a trebuchet prior to flinging the stone against the enemy's stronghold. This 13th Century illumination portrays an Old Testament battle but in contemporary terms. After securing the sling with catches, the warriors weighted the three ropes on the right of the pivot. When the catches were sprung, the weights hurled the stone.

A Bow's Tension Contributes Deadly Accuracy

Just as the forces of torsion and counterpoise contributed to the destructiveness of weaponry, so the force of tension added another group of highly accurate machines to the warrior's arsenal. The first of the tension machines was probably a ballista, or huge crossbow. Very likely the first ones were made in Syracuse in 400 B.C. for a Greek tyrant who became a master of siegecraft in his wars with Carthage. They may have looked like more primitive versions of the 16th Century machine above.

One of the problems that the inventor of the crossbow faced was that he had no good metals to forge the bow; he probably put together a composite of wood, horn and sinew to get maximum spring and strength. A winch or lever arrangement was devised to draw the bowstring.

The ballista achieved great accuracy because of a groove in the stock that corresponded to the barrel of a rifle.

The hand crossbow played a major role in the campaigns of the Middle Ages. Its

CROSSBOW OF CELLINI

A 16th Century crossbow, falsely and inexplicably named after the goldsmith and sculptor Benvenuto Cellini, stands in a courtyard of Castel Sant' Angelo, Rome. From tip to tip the bow measures about 22 feet; the stock is more than 13 feet long. The crossbow was made from chestnut wood and iron, with a string of catgut. Its range was probably about 200 yards.

effectiveness was based on the fact that it allowed an archer to use a bow stronger than he could pull with his arms alone; it brought into play the immensely more powerful muscles of the back and legs. The archer held the bow to the ground with one foot, knelt and attached the bowstring to a hook on his belt. By straightening, he pulled the string into position. In the 14th Century steel bows were introduced that could be pulled only with the help of such a device as the windlass.

Stepping Up the Tempo of Battle with a Mobile Striking Force

In about 2000 B.C., 1,500 or more years after chariots first appeared in battle, a technological breakthrough—the development of the spoked wheel—revolutionized warfare. At the same time the horse replaced the ass as the chariot's motive power. These two innovations converted the first crude carts into effective combat vehicles—the spoked wheel replaced the solid wheel and, by decreasing weight, achieved maneuverability; the horse contributed speed. Using chariots as mobile missile carriers, the Hyksos from Asia defeated the Egyptians about 1730 B.C.

The Egyptian chariots (*opposite*) carried a driver, a bowman and ammunition. Chariot forces could slice into the enemy's ranks and destroy the battle formations or could contain the enemy by sweeping around it while pouring in arrows.

By 1300 B.C., chariots were used in battle from Sweden to China, with variations depending on terrain and style of fighting. The Persians, for example, rated chariots below their superior cavalry, but are credited with introducing the scythed chariot (*lower right*) in about 500 B.C.

The Romans, experts in organized warfare, never developed a chariot force but used the machines for racing and ceremony.

A VEHICLE FOR PAGEANTRY
An Etruscan ceremonial chariot dating from the Sixth Century is a unique restoration now in the possession of New York's Metropolitan Museum of Art. It was used to parade dignitaries and heroes before the populace in much the same fashion as today's heroes are driven in convertibles past admiring crowds. The chariot is large enough to contain the hero and a driver.

LEONARDO'S DEADLY IDEA
Leonardo da Vinci's genius for improving on the ideas of others is shown in this vicious 15th Century scythed chariot. Less efficient models had been in use as long as 2,000 years before. Leonardo also sketched such weapons as a tank carrying breech-loading cannon, a steam gun, a flying machine (and parachute), shrapnel and a machine gun with three tiers of 12 barrels each.

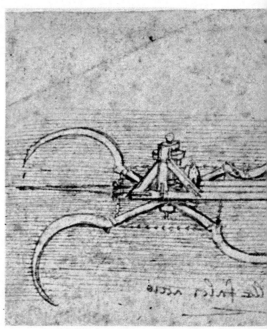

A CHARIOT FOR FIGHTING

King Tutenkhamon of Egypt charges into battle against the Nubians about 1350 B.C. The Egyptian chariots were engineered for fast striking power, with a framework of very light wood and sides of canvas or leather. The wheels were set wide to allow quick turns. The king's bow, of wood veneered with antelope horn, compares favorably with English 16th Century longbows.

The Oar and the Sail: Motive Power for War Machines Afloat

Almost as soon as he learned to walk upright, man learned also to propel himself on a floating log by means of a pole which evolved into a paddle and finally an oar. But these machines, levers all, required hard work. Then, about 3000 B.C., some inventive genius living at the eastern end of the Mediterranean rigged a sail on his craft. He harnessed a power source for seagoing war machines that ruled the main for 49 centuries.

In moving troops and matériel across water, the wind became the ally of every seagoing nation. From ancient times, wind and the sail to harness it carried man to places he had only dreamed of, and enabled him to seize and maintain power.

While the sail moved troops and supplies with uncontested efficiency, the oar remained superior in close combat where wind might prove fickle. Galleys armed with rams and powered by 50 or more oars were deadly in battle. The galleys often sailed to reach the enemy but the sails were stowed for fighting. One of the best was the Greek trireme, a ship with three banks of oars. By the Third Century B.C. multibanked galleys were the fighting ships of most Mediterranean navies. The Romans added to their navy's striking power by devising a portable gangway for boarding enemy ships.

Another weapon which added terror to the war ship's effectiveness was "Greek fire" *(below)*, which apparently made its first appearance about 673 A.D. when Constantine Pogonatus used it to defend his capital against besieging Saracens. The Byzantine emperors kept the formula for the mixture a closely guarded secret. But whatever its composition, it was squirted through tubes, spattering trails of flame.

A galley with oars poised and sail hoisted envelops an enemy ship with "Greek fire" from its bow tube. This Byzantine manuscript uses

AN AMPHIBIOUS OPERATION
A striking force of Christian knights and Genoese mercenaries sails in 1390 to punish the Barbary pirates and to spread the faith. The commander, Louis de Bourbon, is being rowed out to his ship *(lower left)*. This expedition engaged in little heavy fighting but one account says several knights died anyway, roasted to death in their armor beneath the punishing African sun.

a kind of graphic shorthand to chronicle the battle; ships carrying fire-spewing machines were usually manned by upward of 150 sailors.

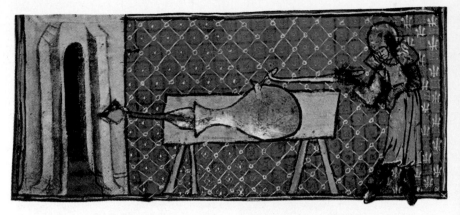

The earliest picture of a gun is a 1326 drawing for the future King Edward III of England.

A Cannon's Roar: The Signal For Vast, Impersonal War

Some time in the early 1300s, a gun was fired in battle for the first time, possibly by the English in an encounter with the Scots at Weardale in 1327. Though many armies resisted the use of the gun for 200 years after this, they eventually had to change or die.

The first guns looked like vases *(above)*, as is reflected in their names, *vasii* and *pots-de-fer*. But very soon cannon of more modern shape appeared *(right)* and by the 15th Century huge siege guns were being constructed *(below)*.

It was also in the 15th Century that the enormous power of the gases suddenly released in the combustion of gunpowder was sufficiently controlled to make handguns practical. The first was the arquebus. Its introduction meant the end to an era in warfare when masses of men armed with pike poles or aristocratic knights on horseback could dominate the battlefield.

POWERFUL BUT AWKWARD
This 12-foot-long cannon shows an early trend toward making bigger and bigger guns. Expensive and awkward, they fell into disuse. The gun was found on Rhodes but was built on the mainland, as shown in the German inscription: "My name is Catherine. Beware of my contents. I punish injustice. George Endorfer cast me. Sigismund, Archduke of Austria. Anno 1404."

UNGAINLY BUT USEFUL
In another scene from the same manuscript shown on page 49, Louis de Bourbon lays siege to a town during a campaign against Barbary pirates in 1390. Although the invaders had cannon, infantrymen still are depicted using crossbows rather than handguns, which did not become common until the 16th Century. The force's firepower helped it to besiege 40,000.

3

The Revolution Fomented by Simple Steam

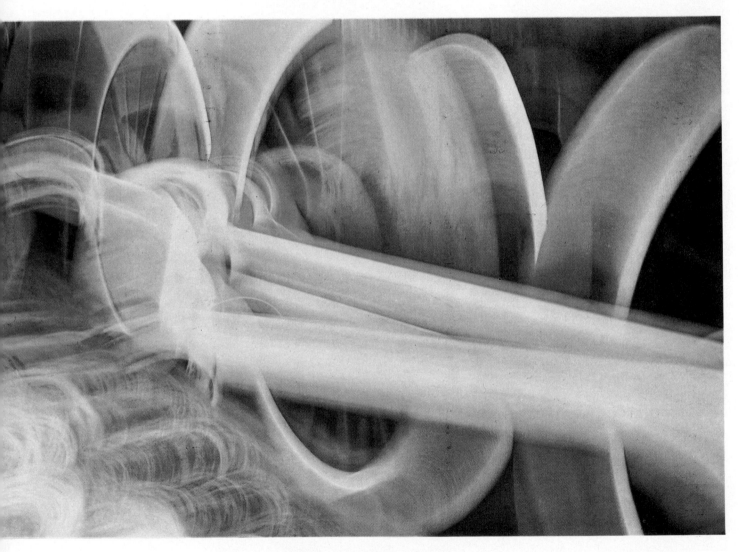

SYMBOL OF AN ERA
Now largely supplanted by diesels, the steam locomotive *(drive wheels above)* provides an increasingly nostalgic symbol of a receding age. Monarch of machines for some two centuries, the steam engine furnished the motive power for both transport and industry, and no amount of technological progress can gainsay its momentous role in the Industrial Revolution.

IN 1685 Sir Samuel Morland, Master Mechanic to King Charles II, submitted for royal perusal a report on an intriguing and possibly valuable reaction of water to heat. "Water being evaporated by fire," he wrote, "the vapours require a greater space, about 2000 times that occupied by the Water. And rather than submit to imprisonment it will burst a piece of ordnance. But being controlled . . . it bears its burden peaceably, like good horses, and thus may be of great use to mankind. . . ."

Prophetic words these, presaging the steam engine; and so presaging, in a nation yet unborn, balloon-stacked freight locomotives crashing up the Sierra canyons above Sacramento, steam-powered ore crushers thundering in Virginia City, factory whistles shrieking over Gastonia, train whistles hooting down the Hudson River Valley, side-wheelers blowing for their Mississippi landings—all sounds of manifest destiny, of a bold young America that never could have happened without the machine called the steam engine and its millions of good, peaceable horses.

Many of us have the impression that the Age of Steam started with the adolescent James Watt. We see him brooding in the kitchen, watching a jet of steam as it lifts the lid of his mother's bubbling teakettle. He puzzles awhile, then suddenly cries, "I've got it!" That very night, he builds the first steam engine.

History, for better or worse, is seldom as simple as the legend, and it accords honors in steam technology to earlier men. There was Hero of Alexandria, whose *aeolipile* was the first known steam-powered contrivance. Then—after more than a millennium in which steam went largely unnoticed—there came the epochal 17th Century discoveries of De Caus, Galileo and Torricelli. Among them they established the facts summed up in Sir Samuel's report: (1) water, when it evaporates, becomes steam; (2) steam expands—a quart of water will boil into about 1,700 quarts of steam; (3) there is raw, sometimes fearsome, power in this expansive force; as easily as it raises a pot lid, it can blow up the boiler or even ironbound cannon that tries to restrain it; (4) when steam cools, it condenses—reverts, that is, to its original state, water; (5) if this process takes place in a closed container, it will create a vacuum in the container.

In England, the condensation-created vacuum fired the imagination of practical men. Many mines troubled by subsurface water were being drained, at nearly prohibitive cost, by horse-powered pumps. Suppose, instead, that a container were placed inside such a mine and a vacuum were created within the container by steam condensation. Would not atmospheric pressure—the weight of the air outside the container—fill the vacuum with the water now being pumped out at such expense? The first usable steam pump to attempt this operation is credited to Captain Thomas Savery, a military engineer. Savery's apparatus, devised about 1698 and called "The Miner's Friend," had an elongated oval tank perhaps the size of a barrel, and was filled with steam from a boiler. The opening of a valve doused cold water on the tank. This condensed the steam and formed a partial vacuum in the tank. Water from the mine sump rushed into the tank through an intake pipe to fill the vacuum. The operator then closed the intake valve, opened the outlet cock, then opened the valve on the steam pipe. This cycle could be repeated five times a minute.

The perils of a friend

Despite its name, "The Miner's Friend" proved not too effective a solution to the mine-flooding problem. Atmospheric pressure alone cannot raise a column of water more than about 33 feet; thus Savery's apparatus had to be placed in a gallery no higher than this above the bottom of the shaft. Working at close quarters with flame and steam in such subterranean cells was perilous. There had to be a better way.

Steam's potential had also fascinated a French physicist, Denis Papin, who turned to and invented the precursor of today's familiar kitchen standby, the steam pressure cooker, and, to keep it from blowing up, also devised the first known safety valve. But whatever his status in culinary circles, Papin's chief distinction in the annals of steam was secured by other means. In 1690 he hit upon the brilliant idea of synthesizing a steam-created vacuum and a piston-and-cylinder mechanism—putting steam to work to move the piston. The result was the first true heat machine in history.

It was simplicity itself, a vertical tube two and a half inches in diameter, fitted with piston and rod, with a little water on the thin metal floor of the tube. Papin heated the water; the rising steam pushed against the piston and raised it to the top of the tube. Papin fastened it there with a catch, allowing the tube to cool; the steam condensed and formed the familiar vacuum. Papin released the catch; atmospheric pressure forced the piston back down the tube to its original position. This, in essence, was the way the steam engine worked for nearly a century until James Watt began using the expansive force of steam to push the piston through its return stroke.

In the interim, in 1712, a young English ironmonger of Dartmouth, Thomas Newcomen, devised a new heat engine—one that, unlike Papin's, could be put to work, could answer the increasingly desperate need to pump water out of deep-shafted mines. A key feature (*left*) was a massive wooden crossbeam, like the balance arm of a pair of scales. At one end hung a pump rod connected to a plunger in the mine below; at the other end was the piston-and-cylinder mechanism, the cylinder perhaps six feet high and up to 40 inches in diameter. Alternately applying steam, then condensing it by cold-water spray, generated an up-and-

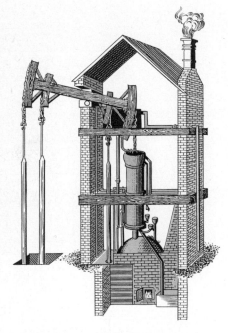

A VORACIOUS CONSUMER OF COAL
Thomas Newcomen's 18th Century heat engine utilized steam to move a piston. This in turn worked a giant horizontal "rocking beam" *(top left)* that pumped water from the Cornish tin mines. Since the machine needed vast quantities of coal to produce relatively little power, it lost out to Watt's more efficient steam engine. But Newcomen is credited with devising the first reliable automatic control —a method of opening and closing valves.

down motion of the piston. This rocked the beam up and down; the beam, in turn, moved the pump rod up and down, operating the pump.

By 1769 nearly 100 of Newcomen's "fire machines" were tilting and wheezing away in England, half of them in the rich "Black Indies" of the Northumbrian coal fields. But fueling them required mountains of coal. It was this drawback that brought a 27-year-old Scotsman named James Watt enduringly to the forefront of machine history.

One day in 1763, Watt, then an instrument maker at the University of Glasgow, was repairing a small bench model of a Newcomen engine. He fell to wondering why it used so much steam and fuel to produce relatively so little power. The engine's inefficiency, obviously, centered about the fact that the cylinder was heated, then cooled, heated, then cooled. But how else to condense the steam? The solution, strikingly uncomplicated, came to Watt in 1765 on a Sunday walk on Glasgow Green. Why not carry the steam off to a separate condensing container? It could be kept cold at all times; the cylinder could then remain as hot as the steam itself throughout every stroke. Heat loss would be eliminated once and for all. "I had not walked further than the Golf-house," Watt recalled later, "when the whole thing was arranged in my mind."

Metamorphosis of a syringe

The next day he started experimenting with a test model. Its piston-and-cylinder was a secondhand surgeon's syringe made of brass, 10 inches long and one and three quarter inches in diameter. He set up his separate condenser; he insulated the cylinder walls with a steam-filled outer casing to help retain the heat; he attached an 18-pound weight to the piston, lit a fire under the little boiler and manipulated the valves, letting steam in, then drawing it off to the condenser. The piston rose and fell, lifting and dropping the heavy weight. Watt's engine worked.

At the start, Watt did not fare well with it. He ran out of money and had to take surveying jobs to get by. His first backer went bankrupt. But finally, when he formed a partnership with Matthew Boulton, a rich Birmingham manufacturer of toys and metal trinkets, his fortunes took a turn for the better. (Ironically, Watt, whose invention changed the face of commerce the world over, himself detested business.)

The new American Republic which was to benefit so abundantly from Watt's genius was just being born the year he built his first commercial engines for an ironworks and a Bloomfield colliery. They were instantly successful. Five years later, in 1781, Consolidated Mines of Cornwall replaced seven Newcomen engines with five of the Boulton and Watt models. Performing the same work, they consumed only 6,100 tons of coal a year to the Newcomen engines' 19,000 tons.

Nevertheless, Watt kept improving his engine, and also devised a means

TAMER OF THE BRUTE FORCE OF WATER ON THE BOIL

A NEEDLESSLY MODEST INVENTOR

While not the originator of the steam engine, James Watt fathered many of the devices that made it a thumping success. One Glasgow professor commended him for his "copiousness of invention." Watt demurred, saying, "I am not so quick as many."

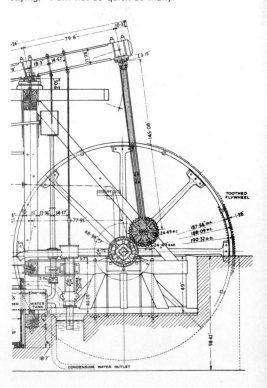

A SUN AND ITS PLANET

The steam engine acquired a host of new uses, such as driving mills or lathes, when its up-and-down motion was converted to rotary motion. Watt's first conversion device was a "sun-and-planet gear" consisting of two meshed cogwheels, the "sun" and "planet" (at center of large flywheel). As the rocking beam (top) swung the shaft (color) up and down, the "planet" moved around the "sun." This action rotated the "sun's" axle.

of giving prospective buyers an idea of its capabilities: he established the horsepower as a standard unit of measure still used to determine the power of machines that have long since sent the working horse to clover.

Thomas Savery, among others before Watt, had fixed upon the work capacity of the horse as a standard of performance. Savery concluded that three horses were needed to keep one at work: one turning the wheel that supplied the power, two standing by as replacements. Consequently, if one of his engines drove a pump that required four horses to power it, he called it a 12-horse engine. Watt took a more scientific approach, declining to consider the idle horses.

An exemplary draft horse

There is a difference, in physics, between the terms *work* and *power*. Work is defined as the overcoming of resistance, and the *amount* of work is measured in foot-pounds. A 200-pound man, climbing a flight of stairs 10 feet high, performs work equal to the pounds he raises times the number of feet he raises them: 200 times 10, or 2,000 foot-pounds. This remains the same whether he climbs the stairs in one minute or one hour. Power, however, takes the time factor into account: it refers to the *rate* at which work is done. It may be expressed by the equation $power = work / time$. If the man climbs the stairs in five seconds, the power he exerts equals 2,000 foot-pounds divided by five, or 400 foot-pounds a second. Watt calculated that a draft horse—Savery had not specified how strong an animal he had in mind—could exert, per minute, 32,400 foot-pounds, a figure he and Boulton later standardized at 33,000. Thus one horsepower was equivalent to 550 foot-pounds per second—about 20 times more than a man could put out in sustained effort.

All that was lacking to make steam the mightiest prime mover yet known was some device for converting the up-and-down, reciprocating stroke of the steam engine's rocking beam into rotary motion. One of Watt's workmen beat him to a patent on the logical solution—a crank and flywheel with connecting rod. The resourceful Watt promptly hit upon an alternative, the "sun-and-planet gear" *(shown on previous page)*.

With vital rotative capacity, steam could now drive wheels, belts and machinery. All a steam engine asked was cheap coal and boiler water. In return it would tirelessly deliver the power of half a dozen waterwheels. Hardheaded industrialists needed no persuasion. By 1824, people everywhere were inclined to agree when Sadi Carnot, a French engineer, remarked that the British Empire would suffer less from the destruction of its entire fleet than from the loss of its chuffing steam engines.

Carnot undoubtedly had in mind an industry by then almost entirely dependent upon steam and regarded as "the sacred staple and foundation" of British wealth: the textile industry. Steam had revolutionized

A STEAMY STROLL
The newfangled use of steam for locomotion inspired both ribaldry and satire. In the 1820s, British cartoonist Robert Seymour drew this sketch of a gentleman encased in a "walking machine." His legs, in two huge cylinders, are powered automatically by a steam engine, enabling him to concentrate on reading a magazine called *New Inventions*.

this industry and in so doing had changed the face of England. Mills no longer nestled along pastoral streams; they rose, barracks-like, eight or nine stories high, wherever there was coal to heat the boilers of their steam engines. Their smokestacks and slums spread a reeking black blight over Lancashire and the Midlands. But they also made Britain the world's richest industrial power, helping to boom her exports from insignificance in 1780 to nearly £8,000,000 sterling just two decades later.

Inventions other than Watt's, of course, contributed to this triumph. The eventful century that had seen the steam engine emerge from the contraptions of Papin and Savery had also seen a dramatic mechanical surge in the textile world. Primitive wheels and looms had been nudged aside by machines that could spin and weave—faster and better than any craftsman—the proud serges of Exeter, the scarlet woolens of Stroud.

Since the time of ancient Troy, the weaver had painstakingly passed his shuttle under and over the warp threads by hand, building up the fabric on the loom as he went. Subsequently, a foot-pedal device had enabled him to raise the odd- or even-numbered warp threads as a set, forming a "shed" through which he could skim the shuttle from one hand to the other. Then, in 1733, John Kay, a weaver and mechanic of Bury, equipped a shuttle with tiny wheels and set it in a grooved rail that could be moved along the frame of the loom. He hung adjustable wooden hammers on each side of the loom and connected them by a cord to a central handle. Now the weaver could sit at the center of the loom and merely pull the handle. This activated a hammer, which rapped the shuttle and sent it "flying" through a shed twice as wide as before.

Impact of a gimcrack

In the same year, a Lichfield carpenter-inventor, John Wyatt, wrote his brother, "I think I have a gymcrak of some consequence." He did indeed. He and his partner, Lewis Paul, contributed a new concept to spinning: the use of mechanical rollers to form a tough, compressed thread that could be stretched out in spinning to any desired fineness.

Some 35 years later, James Hargreaves, a Blackburn carpenter and weaver, developed the first practical spinning machine—the jenny. It was a simple wooden arrangement with two notable features: a crank-and-wheel device by which the spinner could rotate several spindles at once, and a traveling pair of rails, to stretch the threads and twist them at the same time. The smallest, cheapest jenny produced more thread in a day than six or eight human spinners and their handwheels.

No sooner had the jenny relegated the spinning wheel to the attic than along came even bigger and better textile machines. The first was the "water frame" of Richard Arkwright, unforgettably limned by Thomas Carlyle as "that bag-cheeked, pot-bellied, much enduring, much invent-

A BOILER ON WINGS

In this bizarre flying machine, as in the cartoon opposite, Robert Seymour takes another poke at 19th Century technology by lampooning the idea that steam could be used to make man fly. The aviator sits astride a spherical boiler to which webbed wings are attached. Seymour, for reasons lost to history, employed the pseudonym of "Shortshanks."

ing barber" who gave England "the power of cotton." With technical help from a clockmaker and financial help from a barkeep friend, this remarkable figure—who went from barbering and wigmaking to become Britain's first great industrialist-capitalist—made and patented the first spinning machine powered by waterwheel. This machine alone was to have a notable impact on the fledgling American economy. While Arkwright plunged on to riches and knighthood, Samuel Slater, an apprentice in one of his mills, smuggled a version of the water frame to America—in his head. Britain, to protect its cotton trade, had forbidden export of textile machinery or its design. Seeing no future at home, Slater slipped out of England in 1789 disguised as a farmer. In four years, on the site of Pawtucket, Rhode Island, he had built from his extraordinary memory the first successful cotton-spinning mill in the United States. By 1840, American cotton manufactured goods had an annual value of $46 million.

The mileage in a mule

No less a milestone than Arkwright's invention was Samuel Crompton's mule, combining the water frame's rollers and the jenny's movable carriage; its descendants occupy today's great textile mills. One worker with a Crompton mule could spin as much thread in a day as 300 could spin in 1760 with handwheels. Spinning mules driven by water or steam were soon producing literally millions of miles of yarn and thread.

The machines of Britain's Industrial Revolution not only annihilated the past but also shaped the future. They brought opulence and squalor, hope and degradation, Sir Richard Arkwright—and Karl Marx. And even as they spread blessing and bane through the Western world, they reduced its very dimensions by means of steam-powered transportation.

Watt's double-acting steam engine—alternately applying steam and vacuum to opposite sides of the piston—had doubled the cylinder's power. But he had never used high pressures. Later engines did. Faster, more compact, they inspired British experiments with steam locomotives that could replace horses in the hauling of coal from pit to canal barge. The first to put steam on wheels and rails was Richard Trevithick, a Cornish mining engineer; in 1804 his one-cylinder locomotive, with horizontal boiler and piston, pulled 10 tons of bar iron, 70 thrill-seekers and five cars along nine miles of Welsh colliery track in four hours.

In the next 25 years, a picturesque variety of rattling, smoking, piston-pounding iron colts tore up rails, exploded, set fire to the countryside, terrified cattle, amazed the populace—and made railroad history: Timothy Hackworth and William Hedley's twin-cylindered *Puffing Billy*; George Stephenson's twin-cylindered, six-and-a-half-ton *Locomotion No. 1*, which, in 1825, pulled 80 to 90 tons of coal and flour, 400 to 600 people and a brass band at an average speed of eight miles per hour in the

AN EARLY CONTEST WINNER
A glamor queen among early steam locomotives, George Stephenson's *Rocket,* weighing more than seven tons with tender, humbled four rivals in an 1829 competition for the right to work for the new Liverpool & Manchester Railway. At one point during the trial, *Rocket* hit the then meteoric speed of 29 miles per hour. After more than a decade of service, it was retired, horizontal boiler, tall stack and all, to a London museum.

A TRAUMATIC TRAIN RIDE
One of the first trips by rail in the U.S. was an 1831 run between Albany and Schenectady, New York, by the steam conveyance at right. Behind its wood-burning locomotive, the *DeWitt Clinton,* was a flatcar for water and wood; behind that was a stagecoach-like section for passengers. The train's initial jerk knocked most riders out of their seats and sparks from the *Clinton's* smokestack set fire to the umbrellas they had raised as shields.

world's first formal passenger-train ride; Hackworth's elegant *Royal George*, which hauled 22,442 tons of freight over its 20-mile line in a year at a cost of $2,250, less than half the cost of horses for the same work; and Stephenson's black-and-yellow *Rocket (opposite)*, winner of the sensational Rainhill contest in 1829 to determine the locomotive to be used by the new Liverpool & Manchester Railway—fully 35 miles long.

At about this time, however, Americans were brashly beginning to build a Baltimore & Ohio right of way that would cover no less than 300 miles, from Baltimore across the Allegheny wilderness to Wheeling. Challenged by the vast sweep of continent that beckoned endlessly westward, they embraced machines with a special fervor, making them into tools to conquer the land: steam locomotives to master its mountains and deserts, steamboats to ply its winding rivers.

As early as 1786, the eccentric John Fitch built a weird craft propelled, in the manner of a canoe, by 12 steam-driven vertical paddles, six to a side. With a more practical later model, during the summer of 1790 on the Delaware River, he maintained the first steamboat run in America. But it did not pay; the machinery left no room for profitable cargo.

A demoniac profitmaker

It remained for Robert Fulton of Pennsylvania—artist, gunsmith, engineer, inventor—to design, build and operate the first commercially successful steamboat, a flat-bottomed, 100-ton side-wheeler that moved up the Hudson River on her maiden voyage, according to one startled farmer on the bank, "like the Devil on a sawmill." Fulton realistically combined a power plant—a 20-horsepower Boulton and Watt engine driving a paddle-wheel crankshaft—with a hull that could carry profit-making quantities of both passengers and freight. Within two months of her first run between New York and Albany in August 1807, the *North River Steamboat* was carrying 60 to 90 passengers on each trip, covering the 150 miles in 36 hours or less. Within three months, she had earned $1,000 as against her initial cost of $20,000. In time, Fulton renamed her *Clermont*, the name she bears in history.

By 1830, some 230 steamers were churning America's rivers. That same year Peter Cooper drove his midget engine, *Tom Thumb*, with sawed-off musket barrels for boiler tubes, over the first 13-mile stretch of B & O track between Baltimore and Ellicott's Mills. Three years later, the gleaming iron rails snaked all the way to Harpers Ferry, 137 miles north and west—the longest reach of railroad track in the world.

To negotiate the hairpin curves and steep grades of hacked-out mountain roads, Yankee locomotive builders—John B. Jervis, Isaac Dripps, William Harris, Matthias W. Baldwin, the Philadelphia watchmaker, and others—built canny Yankee features into their machines: a swivel-

A GIFT FOR THE MIKADO

Visiting Japan in 1854, Commodore Matthew Perry presented the Mikado with a train which, though undersized, ran perfectly. Among its enthused Japanese viewers was the artist who sketched its locomotive and tender *(right)*. A literal translation of his explanatory text: "The place for smoke to come out." "The place to make whistle." "This [the bell] is the one to hit when running." And, over the tender: "Americans burn coal here."

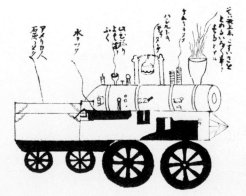

ing, four-wheel, "bogie" truck under the front end; a heavy "cowcatcher"; a closed rear cab for engineer and fireman; a sandbox for slippery tracks; flexible connections for coupling rods that would "give" on curves. Before the industry was 10 years old, the fame of American locomotives had spread abroad. In the 1830s, their manufacturers began to fill orders from Russia, Germany, Austria, Cuba, even England itself. In 1859, the Pasha of Egypt took a 12-hour ride on an Alexandria-Suez Railroad train pulled by his spanking new American locomotive. "God is great," he said when it was over, "but those Yankees are very near perfection."

As the rails pushed west, the Yankees ran head-on into other problems —and solved them. They invented a steam shovel and a steam-powered pile driver. They bored tunnels through mountains, flung spider-web trestles across streams and chasms. "Lay the track first," they cried, "build the road later." By 1860, more than 30,000 miles of track around the country attested to their initiative. Nine years later men drove the Golden Spike at Promontory Point, Utah, joining the Union and Central Pacific tracks, and the rails ribboned America from sea to shining sea.

A mournful whistle blew for the stately Concord coach, the trusty Conestoga wagon, the plodding desert mule trains. A dirgelike bell tolled for the pioneer days and the wild, Western frontier. A horse made of iron had done them in, and he would have his day—while it lasted.

A Prolific Period of Invention

The age of invention, like the Renaissance, dawned in different countries at different times, bringing with it new machines, tools and agricultural techniques. One great invention bred another, beginning in England with Thomas Savery's 1698 steam engine and the application in 1785 of steam power to drive machines for spinning and weaving. On the Continent in the 1800s, French, German and Belgian inventors added the water turbine, internal-combustion engine and electrical generator; while in America, inventions like Whitney's cotton gin, Fulton's steamboat, McCormick's reaper and Morse's telegraph provided the new nation with a technological independence. The following pages picture some of the masterpieces and oddities *(opposite)* of the age, an era when Eli Whitney's idea of interchangeable parts in manufacture, the key to mass production, became known throughout the world as "The American System."

THREE-MASTED COUPE

The gargantuan wind chariot pictured opposite, named *L'Eolienne* by its French inventor, was sped on its way by gusts of wind at its Paris trial run in 1834. This vehicle was one of the most efficient of an adventuresome series which included a windmill-powered carriage. Such exotic forms of land locomotion were, however, eventually abandoned for the modern motorcar.

Savery, Newcomen, Watt: Men Who Made the Great Age of Steam

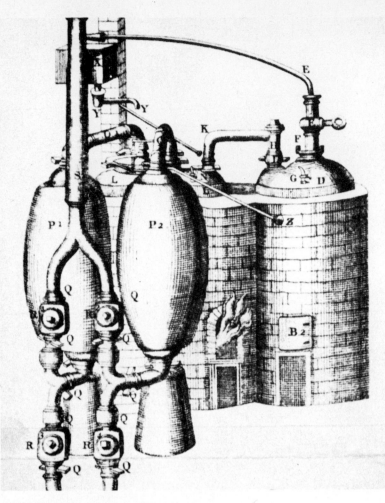

The relentless force of steam, expanding out of boilers, powered the Industrial Revolution. It replaced the feeble, fatigue-ridden muscle power of men and animals and allowed man to do many things that his muscles alone could not do. Steam was first exploited by Thomas Savery and Thomas Newcomen in early 18th Century England in the task of pumping seepage out of mine shafts. Then an ingenious instrument maker named James Watt improved these crude engines, making them more efficient, and converted them into power sources which George Stephenson would use to turn a locomotive's wheels. The early steam engine *was* a limited machine. It was bulky. It was extremely hot and could not be used where fire was a hazard. Yet, it was a measure of the age's inventors that they modified the steam engine so that it could be accommodated in the hulls of small ships.

Steam's power inspired inventive notions in many other men, and soon mills, ships and locomotives through all the Western world were driven by steam. It became so ubiquitous a servant that the period of the Industrial Revolution is also widely called the "Age of Steam." Though steam engines have now passed the prime of their usefulness, their legacy remains. For they first put into man's head the fantastic and fruitful notion of using heat to produce mechanical movement. It is this idea, more than any other, that has shaped our whole technical civilization.

THE MINER'S STEAMY FRIEND
Invented by Thomas Savery in 1698, this machine *(above)* used the vacuum created by condensing steam to suck water out of mine shafts. He called it "The Miner's Friend." Savery's machine could draw water only 32 feet up the shaft. Thomas Newcomen had improved it by 1712.

RIDING "THE CAMEL"
Packed with passengers and ripping along at 6 to 10 mph, the train in this old lithograph *(below)* makes its maiden run over the 20-mile Bodmin Wadebridge line in England in 1834. Named *The Camel,* the steam engine had less endurance than its namesake; it stopped for fuel four times.

THE "CATCH ME WHO CAN"

To show his improved locomotive to the world-ly citizens of London, Richard Trevithick set up in 1808 a circular track *(above)* within an enclo-sure, charging admission at five shillings a head, half an average week's wages. Young bloods rushed to witness the machine's performance.

The "few who were not too timid" rode behind the chugging engine, before a rail broke and it was derailed. Before the disaster, Trevithick had vainly offered to race his engine with any racehorse for an uninterrupted 24 hours to de-termine which would cover the better distance.

ARKWRIGHT'S SPINNING MACHINE

This 32-inch-high machine *(right)* patented by Arkwright could not only spin cotton thread much faster than the old spinning wheel, but it also spun a far stronger thread. It thereby made possible a cloth woven of cotton alone, rather than cotton mixed with flax as in the past.

FATHER OF THE FACTORY SYSTEM

Though often credited with the invention of a spinning machine, Richard Arkwright *(above)* apparently patented a principle devised by others. Acute in business, however, he was the first to develop the revolutionary potential in the factory system, taking textile workers out of their homes.

BEGINNINGS OF MASS PRODUCTION

In this great spinning hall near Lancaster are several of the huge machines used in the early 19th Century to twist cotton into thread. Each machine, with 900 spindles to wind up the thread, is controlled by one man. By the time this picture was made in 1835, the spinning machines devised by Samuel Crompton only 56 years before had developed and spread widely.

The Technological Teamwork of Textiles and Steel

Until 1733, the arts of spinning and weaving had changed little in 7,000 years: they were slow, hand crafts. But then John Kay invented his "flying shuttle" that enabled weavers to weave fabric faster than spinners could make thread. Out of the race that ensued in England between spinners and weavers came a host of machines: James Hargreaves' "spinning jenny" and Richard Arkwright's "water frame," Samuel Crompton's "spinning mule" and Edmund Cartwright's power loom. But these machines, first made of wood, could not have developed far had it not been for the parallel development in England of the metals industry. Tough, light steel in particular was needed, but steel was a rare and costly material, produced through a tedious process of heating and pounding iron. Just in time came fiery new processes for making steel in vast quantities.

THE CONVERTERS

BESSEMER'S INSTANT STEEL

Henry Bessemer invented a new artillery shell but found contemporary cast-iron guns were not strong enough to fire it. So he developed a "converter" *(above)* for removing some of the carbon that weakens cast iron. His converter could produce some 20 tons of steel in 20 minutes.

FIREWORKS FOR ROYALTY

The spectacular performance of a Bessemer converter enthralled the Prince and Princess of Wales during a visit to Sheffield in 1875. The converter's display is the product of a blast of air pumped through the molten iron, burning off excess carbon to produce low-carbon steel.

FATHER OF THE FOUR-STROKE
In developing the complex but efficient four-stroke internal-combustion engine widely used today, the self-educated German mechanic Nikolaus Otto *(above)* put into practice the theories of a Frenchman, Alphonse Beau de Rochas. These theories, in turn, dealt with ways to improve Lenoir's engine, whose running costs had proved excessive compared with steam engines'.

THE INTRICATE OTTO CYCLE
An Otto-type four-stroke engine, such as this 35-horsepower version of 1893, increased its efficiency by compressing the fuel vapor in its cylinders before igniting it. These improved internal-combustion engines were not only lighter and quicker-starting than steam engines, but also provided a workable machine which could use as a power source the energy of petroleum.

EARLY FRUITS OF AUTOMATION
Before Joseph Marie Jacquard invented his loom for weaving designs in 1804, large numbers of workers had been needed to pull the cords that controlled pattern-weaving silk looms in France. Jacquard's own health had been damaged by this arduous work, but it was almost ruined completely as workers in Lyon rioted over the unemployment that his loom brought.

On the Continent
Progress:
Slow but Sophisticated

In Europe the Industrial Revolution proceeded at a more leisurely pace than it did in America and Britain. Part of this lag was due to higher costs of both machinery and raw materials; scattered factories instead of concentrated industries; and internal customs barriers and river tolls. Yet, a group of continental inventors was conceiving machines just as ingenious as those that had sparked the Revolution in Britain and the United States.

Unconcerned with plain cotton, the Frenchman Joseph Marie Jacquard (opposite, below) made a remarkable loom for weaving intricate patterns in fine silk. It used punched cards to produce the patterns and thus foreshadowed the automation to come 150 years later.

The continentals also searched for better, less cumbersome power sources than the fuel-eating steam engine. One Frenchman, Benoît Fourneyron, invented a high-efficiency water turbine. Another, Étienne Lenoir, created the first internal-combustion engine. It was vastly improved by the German, Nikolaus Otto (opposite). Finally, electricity was successfully utilized to power the wheels of progress by the Belgian, Zénobe Gramme (right).

ELECTRICITY'S CONJURER
This statue in Liége honors the development of the first practical industrial dynamo by the Belgian, Zénobe Gramme, in 1876. Gramme's machine used the mechanical power of steam engines to turn coils of wire in a magnetic field and produce electricity. The same machine, powered by electricity, became a motor converting electric power back to mechanical.

In America, a New System Called Mass Production

The ferment of the European Industrial Revolution had its counterpart in America. But Yankee ingenuity added its own flavor. For all the while they were devising new machines, America's inventors were also inventing a system, now known as mass production. It was known throughout the world as "The American System." Its success depended upon a division of labor and the use of machinery to make uniform, interchangeable parts.

Conditions in expanding America well suited the new system: a large demand by settlers for manufactured articles coupled with a scarcity of skilled artisans to make them. Mass production spread with fantastic success all over the Western world. But along with the benefits of the machine age came unfortunate abuses, such as the grinding exploitation of children (*opposite*).

HOME OF THE AMERICAN SYSTEM
Eli Whitney's Arms Manufactory at Hamden, near New Haven (*above*), the first factory using mass production, sits in pleasant rural surroundings beside a stream. Whitney was a benevolent employer who provided his staff of "steady, sober people" with neat houses near the factory.

IDENTICAL LOCOMOTIVES
In the assembly hall of the Borsig Machine Factory, Berlin, Germany (*below*), in 1848, workers assemble locomotives from parts manufactured in other sections of the plant by machine-tool methods. Such techniques also permitted easy, fast and inexpensive repairs on all machinery, since broken or outworn parts could be quickly replaced by spares ordered from the factory.

LITTLE WALLPAPER MAKERS
A woodcut *(left)* from a German newspaper of 1858 shows boys working wallpaper machines. Often children were the sole support for whole families; the children's value, some observers believe, accounted for a rapid rise in European birthrate after the coming of the factory system.

CHILD OF THE FACTORY SYSTEM
One little girl tending a spinning machine, such as the one below in an unknown United States location, could produce as much thread as hundreds of spinners a century before. One of her jobs was to retie the threads when they accidentally broke. Children were often employed because they could be paid lower wages to perform the mechanical and monotonous tasks.

Yankee Genius Explodes in Inspired Gadgetry

"I could make anything a body wanted—anything in the world, it didn't make any difference what; and if there wasn't any quick new-fangled way to make a thing, I could invent one. . . ." This aggressively self-confident statement of faith by Mark Twain's Connecticut Yankee could stand as a credo for all the inventive geniuses of 19th Century America. Blessed with egotism, determination and showmanship, they sold their gadgets—and often became wealthy—despite opposition from the conservative and the suspicious.

Robert Fulton, Cyrus McCormick and Samuel Morse made little contribution to scientific theory. Their inventions themselves were little more than modifications and amalgamations of other men's. Nevertheless, it was their genius for synthesis and their ability to arouse enthusiasm and financing that made commercial successes of their dreams. Without such men, the revolution in industry, farming, communication and travel would still have happened, but with less explosive verve.

BIZARRE MACHINE UP IN THE AIR
In 1878 the citizens of Hartford, Connecticut, saw Professor C. F. Ritchell (*above*) crossing overhead on his "flying bicycle." Held up by a blimp, the contraption was given forward motion by a chain-driven propeller. After flying for an hour, Ritchell felt his legs tiring and descended.

FULTON'S FIRST STEAMBOAT
Robert Fulton's steamboat, the *Clermont*, was not an innovation. Twenty-one years before its maiden voyage up the Hudson in 1807, John Fitch had demonstrated a similar vessel. Fulton's great contribution was a better hull design that made his ship economically feasible. A surprised witness of its trial run shouted that the devil was going upriver to Albany in a sawmill.

ELECTRIC WORDS FROM THE BIBLE
After years of lobbying Congress, Morse was finally given $30,000 by the government to set up a telegraph line from Washington to Baltimore. Below is a later model of his sample machine, which, on May 24, 1844, tapped out in a dot-and-dash code: "What hath God wrought!"

MORSE: PAINTER AND INVENTOR
Samuel Morse *(left)*, whose name will always be linked with telegraphy, was also an accomplished painter. The main features of the telegraph were developed by two contemporaries, Joseph Henry and Leonard Gale, but it was Morse who successfully synthesized their ideas.

PLOWSHARES INTO WEAPONS
The reaper, and later the harvester, which Cyrus McCormick perfected, manufactured and then merchandised with modern business techniques including installment buying, changed the nation's economy and helped win a war. The West became a bountiful wheatland after the reaper provided the means for quick, cheap gathering of crops. The food and prosperity which the invention brought the North was one decisive factor in the Union's victory over the Confederacy.

71

A UNION OF STEAM AND STEED

This drawing of an American-built street locomotive made a newsworthy item in a German illustrated newspaper of 1876. The curious ancestor of the streetcar, it ran on tracks and was powered by steam from a boiler heated by burning gas. The carved figure of a horse attached to the front of the chariot was intended to calm the fears of any jittery horses on the street.

Crowning a Century
of Independence
and Creative Ingenuity

In 1876 the United States celebrated the centennial of its independence by mounting a great exhibition in Philadelphia, the city where the Declaration had been signed. To the delighted surprise of officials, not only all the states—37 at the time—but also many nations from Asia, Europe and South America wanted to participate. Nearly 10 million people saw the exhibition.

Now that the Civil War and the Reconstruction period were safely in the past, the nation's industries surged with new vigor and prosperity. Production spiraled up. New machines and new techniques often were barely installed before they were improved by other inventors. It was a period of creative excitement and an age of mechanical power.

The most dramatic symbol of power at the fair was the huge Corliss steam engine, which provided power for all the other machines at the fair. And while Americans were gaping at the mechanical achievements around them, Europeans were perfecting even more marvels. In the same year as Philadelphia's exhibition Zénobe Gramme (page 67) designed his commercially successful generator; Paul Jablochkoff invented a new kind of arc light; and Nikolaus Otto (pages 66, 67) perfected his internal-combustion engine. The exhibition was, in the words of the Atlantic Monthly, ". . . evidence of man's creative powers . . . Prometheus unbound."

A MECHANICAL GIANT

The 700-ton Corliss steam engine (opposite) was the most powerful machine in the world in 1876. Situated in the middle of Machinery Hall at the exposition, the engine had cylinders more than a yard in diameter and the largest cut gears ever produced. President Ulysses S. Grant and the Emperor of Brazil, Dom Pedro, opened the exhibition by starting the engine.

BREAKING THE SOUND BARRIER

Alexander Graham Bell spoke the first words on the new telephone connection between Chicago and New York on October 18, 1892. The apparatus which he used (above) was a greatly improved version of the primitive model which he had first exhibited in Philadelphia at the centennial. By 1900, half of the American people were within easy distance of a telephone.

4

Assembly-line
Avenues
to Abundance

CHEAPER BY THE THOUSANDS
Presaging today's mass-production techniques, Henry Ford's assembly line of 1913 *(above)* ended outside the plant when Model T bodies were skidded down a ramp and dropped on completed chassis driven out from under the ramp. Primitive as it was, Ford's original operation helped change motoring from a rich man's indulgence to an average man's pastime.

THIS SIDE OF WARFARE, Americans may never know how strong, smart, fast, efficient and tough their country is until they see mass production in action on a heavy-industry assembly line.

Picture a plant sprawled across an area the size of 30 or 40 football fields. Every inch of floor space not essential for passageway or unassembled parts is crammed with machinery to turn out still another machine—an automobile, say, at the rate of one a minute every minute, 60 minutes every hour, 16 hours every day. In this iron jungle, there are machines that hammer, drill, weld, punch, polish, paint, fasten, lift, carry, shear, pound, tighten; ear-shattering machines that whine, scream, bang and clatter. Thousands of machines and men unite in a wild orchestration of heat, power, flesh, metal, sparks, noise and motion. And around and through and above them flow the conveyors and monorails of the assembly line and its tributaries, at an inexorable 20 feet a minute.

To the outsider, the scene seems born of an engineer's delirium. In reality it is a masterpiece of timing, coordination, purpose. Every second is accounted for. Every motion is documented by study. Every machine does one thing, over and over. Every man performs one function, over and over. Mustered here for use on this shift, for each car assembled on this day, in this particular plant at Willow Run, are 13,500 parts: engines, transmissions, springs, gears, axle housing, differential housing, shafts, brake drums, foam rubber, gaskets, locks, radios, tires and all the rest. Many of the parts themselves have been fitted together on sub-assembly lines of their own, in towns near and far. Yet, as a car takes shape, the rocker panel below the door fits the side panel, the side panel fits the door, the wheel fits the axle, the axle fits the frame; the automatic welding guns take 60 seconds to make 45 welds along the underbody; the workers take 60 seconds to install the springs. The car rolls off the line lights on, signals flashing, horn blowing, windshield wipers beating, two metered gallons of gas in the tank—ready to go.

Twenty feet behind it comes another car, and 20 feet behind that comes another car.

"As American as the husking bee," one authority has said of mass production. It is, indeed, deep in the American matrix, an indispensable means toward such basic national goals as a strong economy, a high standard of living and the defense of our freedom.

As far back as the Civil War, mass production of iron, steel, Rodman smoothbore cannons, Springfield rifled muskets, shoes, uniforms and canned goods enabled the Union to defeat the technology-starved South. "Take our word for it," the *Philadelphia Inquirer* editorialized in 1861, "these [Yankee] geniuses will yet produce some patent Secession-Excavator, some Traitor-Annihilator, some Rebel-Thresher, some Confederate State Milling Machine, which will grind through, shell out, or slice up this war, as if it were a bushel of wheat, or an ear of corn, or a big apple." And that is about what they did.

In World War II, retooled American assembly lines turned out 200,000 tanks, 300,000 planes and enough ships to bridge the oceans. Only assembly-line principles made possible the secret manufacture of atomic bomb components in scattered plants and their final, fateful assembly at Los Alamos.

Now, in peacetime, only the creative and mass use of great gangs of precision machines could supply the huge, insatiable demand for products from golf balls to computers, paper plates to jet engines and, above all, for the automobile, truck and bus, of which some eight million were produced in 1963 alone.

A close-knit quintet

Assembly-line production was a long time coming. Men groped for it in dusty English and European workshops in the 1700s, sensed its potential in American factories in the 1800s, and finally achieved it in Henry Ford's plant at Highland Park, Michigan, in 1913. It represents a complex synthesis of five elements: *division of labor,* breaking down the production process into separate tasks performed by specialists (men, machines, or both) who do nothing else; *standardization of parts,* so that they can be mass-produced by machines both for interchangeability and for assembly by unskilled or semiskilled workers; *precision-tooling,* which makes such standardization possible through dies, molds or machines faithfully rendered according to blueprints specifying dimensions as fine as thousandths of an inch; the *assembly line* itself, the line-flow method of moving the work from one worker or machine to the next, evenly, serially, much like the parade of ducks in a shooting gallery.

The fifth element has less to do with mechanics than with desire. If no *mass demand* exists or looms for a product, no one goes to the expense of assembling the machines and mass-producing it.

The first of the five elements to appear was division of labor. This had existed in a primitive way in the cottage production of British textiles before the Industrial Revolution: womenfolk carded wool and spun it into yarn; the man of the house wove it into cloth. Then, in 1700, Christopher Polhem established at Stjernsund, Sweden, a metal-products factory which employed as many as 200 workers, either hired because of a particular skill or trained to operate a particular machine.

Polhem, a brilliant pioneer of technology and author of some 20,000 manuscripts on subjects ranging from textile machinery to an original theory about the creation, has been called "the Archimedes of the North." An ardent nationalist, he hated to see Sweden produce top-grade iron, steel and copper, export them, then buy them back in metalware

THE SHAPE OF THINGS TO COME

Anticipating the conveyor belt so vital to mass production today, this so-called "traveling band"—shown above in a contemporary magazine woodcut—was in use in 1890 at a Pittsburgh foundry for the manufacture of small castings for railway brakes. The "band" was actually a series of tables linked together to form a continuous surface. Put on wheels, they were then moved on a track through the casting, molding and other foundry rooms.

products at vastly increased prices. Arguing for home manufacture, he wrote: "Never take anything out of the country which could be used to make a profit for your people. Let your need and your pride serve as a guide so that everything will be made in your own country."

The term "mass production" had not yet been coined, but Polhem went straight to a principle that, 200 years hence, would inspire Henry Ford: the lower the production costs, the lower the price, the greater the demand. Polhem proposed to cut production costs, as Ford later did, by substituting, wherever possible, machine labor for human labor, and mechanical power—in 18th Century Sweden, waterpower—for manpower. Partly with financial help from the government, he built a series of mills near a tumbling stream between two lakes. The main structure was a huge blacksmith shop and mill more than 100 yards long. Its seven waterwheels drove nine or more drop hammers, as well as various shearing and rolling mills of Polhem's personal design. Other buildings housed a sawmill, a flour mill and a granary. There were also a nail works, a lock works, a clock works and a tin-plating shop.

The staggering array of items mass-produced—and for the most part machine-produced—at Stjernsund during its peak years in the 1720s included pots, pans, mortars, plates, tankards; hand tools for carpenters, blacksmiths, sculptors; clocks, locks, plates, bowls, spoons, knives, forks, steel presses, turnspits, army cots, sheet-iron roofing and gutters, screws, bolts and ornamental brasswork. Polhem's own inventive bent served to speed this torrent. To fashion sheet-iron dishes, for example, he devised a series of mechanical hammers lifted by cams on a horizontal shaft turned by waterwheel. A cast-iron drop hammer shaped and molded the white-hot metal blank, which was then finished by a machine of five smaller hammers: three to finish the edges of a plate, two the interior. These machines turned out the remarkable total of 15 dozen dishes a day.

Many of Polhem's machines were far in advance of his time, and when he died at 90, Stjernsund fell into disuse. The demand for mass-production machinery on the same scale was not to re-emerge until the American Civil War. Meanwhile steam supplanted waterpower, inventors outside Sweden built their own machines, and Polhem's memory faded.

Portents in a common pin

But the impetus toward mass production persisted. In 1762, Jean-Rodolphe Perronet, the engineer who built the Pont de la Concorde in Paris, wrote a fascinating analysis of a factory in L'Aigle, France, where common brass pins were made. Detailing the division of labor, Perronet also made some observations remarkable for the way they anticipated modern time-motion studies of workers in action. Of the pinhead stamping process, for one, he noted, "A man can stamp in one minute 20 pin-

A SWEDISH MEDAL OF HONOR
This medal, struck in Sweden shortly after his death in 1751, honored the mechanical genius of Christopher Polhem and exhorted the nation to recognize his preeminence. Many of his innovations in large-scale manufacturing later were ignored, but in his lifetime his accomplishments so impressed the King of England and Czar of Russia that both tried to lure him to their countries with lucrative offers. An intense patriot, Polhem declined.

heads mixed thick and fine; and as he strikes each head 5 or 6 times, the anvil receives from 100 to 120 blows per minute. A stamper usually prepares 1,000 pins in an hour, and from 10-12,000 in a day." As Perronet's august contemporary, Adam Smith, wrote in *The Wealth of Nations*, 10 unskilled men, each working independently, would be hard put to make one pin each in a day, or 10 in all; but team 10 men under one factory roof with the labor divided, and they can produce upward of 48,000.

One of the first major industries to seize upon division-of-labor techniques to speed production was the food industry, since its operations progressed in well-defined steps. One vivid eyewitness report on a Cincinnati pork-packing house in the 1850s has come down from Frederick Law Olmsted, the landscape architect. Four men—two to lift and turn the carcasses and two to swing the cleavers—comprised, in Olmsted's words, "a sort of human chopping machine," functioning with the mindless efficiency of cogwheels: "By a skilled sleight-of-hand, hams, shoulders, clear, mess, and prime fly off, each squarely cut to its own place, where attendants, aided by trucks and dumb-waiters, dispatch each to its separate destiny—the ham for Mexico, the loin for Bordeaux." Astounded, Olmsted clocked the elapsed time from the moment one hog hit the table until the next took its place—35 seconds.

The second element of assembly-line production—standardized or interchangeable parts—first took hold in the late 1700s. One expert gunsmith might fashion an entire musket in a week; one unskilled workman could not, but if each of a group of unskilled workmen, over the same period, were to make nothing but one identical part all day long, together they would turn out enough locks, stocks and barrels to be assembled into a considerable number of muskets.

Tip-off from a statesman

In 1785 a French gunsmith named LeBlanc, showing work in progress to Thomas Jefferson, then American Ambassador to France, sorted the standardized parts of 50 musket locks into compartments. He then suggested that his visitor pick parts at random from each compartment and put them together. So doing, Jefferson assembled several locks. No mean spare-time tinkerer himself, he was enough impressed to write home to Secretary of Foreign Affairs John Jay: "An improvement is made here in the construction of muskets, which it may be interesting to Congress to know, should they at any time propose to procure any. It consists in the making every part of them so exactly alike, that what belongs to any one, may be used for every other musket. . . ." Further, added Jefferson: "He [LeBlanc] effects it by tools of his own contrivance, which . . . abridge the work, so that he thinks he shall be able to furnish the musket two livres cheaper than the common price."

French arsenals, however, must have been well-stocked with muskets; LeBlanc had trouble finding backers. No one seems to have thought of adapting the idea of interchangeable parts to some other product. But for the new American nation, desperate for skilled labor, it was a production principle that was to help forge a way of life.

The story of Eli Whitney, not only inventor of the cotton gin but also generally acknowledged as father of standardized parts in mass production, is now a classic chapter in the folklore of American technology: how in the late 1790s, when war with France threatened, he undertook to fill a government contract for 10,000 muskets within the wildly improbable limit of two years, how he spent the time tooling up his plant at Whitneyville in Hamden, Connecticut, and how, finally, he set up a millful of waterpowered machines, each repetitively performing one predetermined step in the fabrication of identical, interchangeable parts.

A nephew's nose for news

No detailed description of these machines survives; Whitney applied for no patents, freely sharing his know-how. The only extant firsthand account of his landmark factory—truly the birthplace of American mass production—is contained, curiously, in an imperfect but exuberant letter written by his 10-year-old nephew, Philos Blake: "Thare is a drilling machine and a boureing machine to bour berels and a screw machine and too great large buildings, one nother shop and a stocking shop to stocking guns in, a blacksmith shop and a trip hammer shop." The weapon Whitney was making was a Charleville musket of a type France had supplied to the Colonial Army. It consisted of some 50 parts. A number of those comprising the firing lock were of irregular contour, and it is probable that for these Whitney designed special jigs and templates—metal patterns to guide his drilling, filing and milling machines.

In any event, after heartbreaking delays and numerous time-extensions from sympathetic and farsighted Washington officials, including Jefferson himself, Whitney started heavy production in 1803. His plant turned out 1,000 muskets a year, three times as many as skilled gunsmiths could produce by hand in the government's Springfield Armory. In 1807, his peak year, he produced 2,000—a signal triumph for Whitney's insistence that machines could be devised which would, as he put it, "preclude the necessity of every workman's being bred to the business."

Whoever applied Whitney's interchangeable-parts system to his own mill or shop transformed an industry. About 1807 Eli Terry, a Connecticut neighbor, accepted an order to produce 4,000 wooden clocks. Townsmen in Plymouth considered him daft. He spent one year tooling up his shop, installing lathes and jigs and templates for cutting, sawing and shaping interchangeable wooden parts. The second year he produced

PRODUCTION HIGH ON THE HOG

To help appease America's appetite during the 19th Century, assembly-line methods were applied to every phase of pork-processing. Here hog carcasses are being hung on trolleys and passed on for disemboweling and cleaning. Pork-packing became big business in 1850; by 1873, when this cartoon appeared in *Harper's Weekly,* an up-to-date plant employed 150 men to handle 1,500 hogs a day, while the industry's annual output was 5.5 million.

1,000 clocks, the third year 3,000. His labor and operating costs were so low that he could sell the clocks for four dollars each and still manage to bank a profit.

By the 1850s, the standardized part, produced in whatever quantity the order warranted, symbolized alert American industrial practice. The machine began to appear as the whirring, shining, effortless giver of cornucopian plenty, the magic key to abundance that enabled manufacturers to supply eager hordes of consumers both at home and abroad with products of Yankee enterprise: the Colt revolver, the McCormick reaper, the Day & Newell bank lock, the sewing machine, the typewriter, the safety bicycle and, ultimately, the universal motor car.

It was not quite that simple, of course. For all the miracle of the interchangeable-parts system, Whitney, Colt and the others would never have turned a wheel without certain other advances, independent but interacting. One was the invention, around the start of the 19th Century, of new methods of producing and working iron, steel and brass. These methods made possible the fabrication of metal machinery, which in turn made possible the mass production of metal parts for other machines. Another was the development of the capacity to achieve ever finer degrees of accuracy in machines and machine parts. James Watt's partner, Matthew Boulton, was delighted in 1776 to receive deliveries of steam-engine cylinders whose bore erred no more than "the thickness of an old shilling." By Whitney's time, 25 years later, American machines could fashion relatively complicated lock plates, screws and other musket parts to fit together with little or no filing. (Today some automobile parts are precisioned-machined to accuracies of two thousandths of an inch.)

Perhaps most important was the continuing development of machines to meet the pressures of mass production itself. These were the "machine tools," or "machines that make machines": the lathes, grinders, cutters, shapers, planers, millers, borers, slotters, hammers and punches that carved, ground, drilled, pounded, pressed, scraped and shaved the iron and steel parts that would be assembled into other machines intended for consumer or industrial use.

Mastery in a hammer

In 1839, for example, specifications of the steamer *Great Britain* called for an iron paddle-wheel shaft 30 inches in diameter, to be forged out by hammer on an anvil. Old-fashioned waterpowered tilt hammers could not be raised high enough; the force of their blow could not be controlled. One of Britain's great machine-tool makers, the Scottish-born James Nasmyth, solved the problem by inventing a mighty yet wondrously simple steam hammer *(sketch opposite)* that was to be his masterpiece. Later, Nasmyth increased its power by making it double-acting. The hammer

A CLASSIC FIGURE IN AMERICAN TECHNOLOGY

COTTON GINS AND MUSKETS

Eli Whitney *(above)* was mechanically inclined even as a boy—when on his father's Massachusetts farm he forged nails and hatpins for local sale. His cotton gin, invented when he was only 27, took just 10 days to design and build, but launched a new and fruitful era in agriculture. Later Whitney turned gunmaker and produced 10,000 Charleville muskets *(below)* by using a system of interchangeable parts which was to become a basic feature of American industrial practice.

enormously extended the range of heavy-industry forgings, making possible production of iron plates and beams bigger than ever.

Another towering British figure in the advance of technology was Henry Maudslay, who began his career as an 18-year-old blacksmith at Woolwich Arsenal. A creative machinist, he used his tools as a painter uses his brush or a sculptor his chisel. One of his craftsmen once said of him, "It was pleasing to see him handle a tool of any kind, but he was quite splendid with an 18-inch file." Maudslay won immortality in machine history by elevating the humdrum lathe to one of the most vital machine tools of his time and since. His two salient improvements were all-metal construction (until then the machinery had been fixed to a wooden frame) and an improved slide rest that took the place of human hands in holding the tool in a viselike clamp as it cut into the spinning workpiece. Hands might waver, ease up, overcompensate, press too hard. Now prolonged, dependable, hair-fine accuracy was possible.

A new turn for the lathe

Momentous as it was, Maudslay's slide rest soon revealed its flaw: it could accommodate only one tool at a time, and to change it the workman had to stop the lathe, unclamp this tool, install the next one and start up again. About 1850 three Americans, Frederick W. Howe, Richard S. Lawrence and Henry D. Stone, devised a lathe in which the slide rest was replaced by a rotating vertical turret which held up to eight cutting tools. Locked into position before machining started, they were brought successively into use, as needed, simply by turning the turret from one station to the next. Machine tooling took another giant step toward Detroit and Willow Run.

How far America had traveled along the technological road within a brief century was spectacularly underscored in Machinery Hall at Philadelphia's Centennial Exposition of 1876, commemorating the nation's hundredth birthday. Aglitter with nickel-plated chandeliers, alive with the whirring wheels and rotating shafts of some 8,000 machines—from the 2,500-horsepower Corliss steam engine to midget sewing machines one foot square—the 14-acre wood-and-glass edifice mesmerized native and foreign visitors alike. A German journalist reported: "The essential element in the life of North Americans—the MACHINE—which has enabled them to replace laborious handwork, to mass-produce everything . . . is overwhelmingly presented here." The exhibits showed "a picture of a wild chase . . . after material gain. But who can deny," he concluded, "that there is herein greatness and power?"

Everywhere an American industrialist turned in the 1870s and 1880s he found proof of old Ben Franklin's adage that "time is money." Machines, speeding production, were cutting costs. New machines to spin,

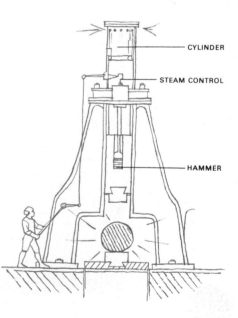

A MIGHTY MASS-PRODUCER

By his own account, James Nasmyth, inventor of the revolutionary steam hammer, fixed on its details in less than an hour. His sketch of it *(above)* shows two upright standards—to guide the hammer—supporting an overhead cylinder, whose piston was connected to the hammer head. Steam admitted to the cylinder raised piston and hammer; release of a steam valve by the operator brought the hammer crashing down on the forging.

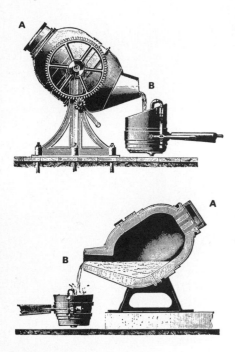

BREAKTHROUGH IN STEEL

Steel began to supplant iron in the machines and structures of the mid-19th Century when men learned to produce it in quantity. In England, Henry Bessemer devised a converter *(side view at top, cross section below)* which blows air from a "wind box" *(A)* through molten pig iron while the converter is upright; this burns off most of the iron's carbon, leaving steel. The converter is then tipped and the steel is poured off at the mouth *(B)*.

twist and test silk thread reduced from $4.50 to less than one dollar the cost of converting a pound of raw silk into loomable material. Newfangled stitchers, rounders, buffers, trimmers and other specialized machines turned out millions of pairs of shoes selling for as low as two dollars a pair, while the price of handmade shoes still ranged upward of $15. Machine gains in the corn and wheat country were even more dramatic. Not long before, a farmer would plod down a furrow with a sack of seed corn around his neck and measure out three grains to a hill; now, with a machine, he planted two rows at a time and 12 to 15 acres a day.

As machine labor replaced man labor, there came the streamlining of the physical process of production itself. And herein lay the beginnings of the assembly line.

An assembly line integrates the actions of men and machines, and imposes on them a time-motion discipline some call tyranny. (In Detroit, a visitor asked a plant superintendent if a worker who made a mistake could stop the assembly line. He might as well have suggested heaving a brick through the Rose Window at Chartres. "That," came the solemn answer, "would be the crime of crimes.") The line blends men and machines into a kind of supramachine whose blind, mechanical function is to turn out an endless series of standardized products. Be the product bread or bombers, the major principle at work is motion—the steady, unremitting movement of the product through successive stages from raw material or components to finished item, while humans or machines or both, stationed along the line, do something to it as it goes past.

Travels of a hog

The line-flow principle established itself first in food processing, after the Civil War. The raw materials were light, relatively easy to handle, simple to convey on a moving line; the end products could come out of the factory, by the carload, in standardized qualities and containers: loaves of bread, bags of flour, cans of beef. During the same era the meat packers of Cincinnati, then nationally known as "Porkopolis," began to make use of the principle of the traveling overhead crane. The hogs were slaughtered, scalded and scraped, then hung by the hamstrings from conveyors on an overhead rail. By this means the carcasses were smoothly rolled from one operator to the next, to be split open, disemboweled, hosed out, inspected, stamped and hauled off into cold storage.

As the system spread to other food processors, consumer costs tumbled. Said Senator George Vest of Missouri in 1890, "Years ago canned foods were delicacies, but today they are the poor man's food, being cheaper in the can than in the green articles."

The line-flow idea also moved into heavier industry. Production engineers, confronted by what seemed irreducible machine schedules, now sought speed-up through the elimination of waste effort and motion in human beings. Armed with stop watch, Frederick W. Taylor ascertained, for instance, that Bethlehem Steel coal shovelers performed at peak— the heft seemed just right—when the shovelful weighed 21 pounds. From then on, all Bethlehem shovelers used shovels that held 21 pounds. The husband-and-wife team of Frank B. and Lillian M. Gilbreth studied the structure, form and geometry of people at work—surgeons, ballplayers, bricklayers. Gilbreth attached lights to their hands and photographed them; then he made wire models of the luminous telltale paths on the photograph, so that the subjects could study their movements and make them more efficient. Discovering in one instance that bricklayers bent over every time they picked up a brick, Gilbreth recommended adjustable platforms to keep the supply within easy reach; bricklaying shot up from 1,000 to 2,700 bricks a day.

A climax of wizardry

The living assembly line itself emerged unmistakably in 1913, in the Highland Park automobile factory of the automotive wizard, Henry Ford. It was Ford, with help from Charles E. ("Cast-iron Charlie") Sorensen and other production men, who finally consolidated the line into the phenomenon it is today. The car involved was the now historic Model T, fabricated of some 5,000 standardized and interchangeable parts, and available, as Ford announced dryly, in any color of the rainbow "so long as it is black."

Soon after he started, Ford effected Assembly Line Principle No. 1: take the work to the men instead of the men to the work. He also established two efficiency procedures harking back to the early studies by Taylor and Gilbreth: no worker ever had to take more than one step, if it could be avoided; no worker ever had to stoop over.

One man, doing the job from A to Z, had turned out one magneto assembly in 20 minutes. When Ford spread the process over 29 operations, assembly time dropped to 13 minutes 10 seconds. Raising the height of the line eight inches brought it within more convenient reach, and cut the time to seven minutes. Adjustments in line speed further reduced it to five minutes.

Assembling a chassis by the stationary method had taken 12 hours 28 minutes. When the chassis was raised waist-high and mechanically drawn past assembly workers at the right speed, the time dropped to 1 hour 33 minutes. The line moved at six feet a minute through 45 stations. "The first men," Ford wrote, "fasten four mud-guard brackets to the chassis frame; the motor arrives on the tenth operation. . . . The man who places a part does not fasten it. . . . The man who puts in a bolt does not put on the nut; the man who puts on the nut does not tighten it. On operation number thirty-four the budding motor gets its gasoline; it has previously received lubrication . . . and on operation number forty-five the car drives out onto John R. Street."

Both Ford and the fervent new motoring public had reason to approve. As production climbed from 78,440 in 1911-1912 to 785,432 in 1916-1917, Model T's price plummeted from $690 to $360—a 47 per cent drop.

Since Ford, both products and assembly lines have multiplied beyond reckoning; American manufacturers of machine tools turn out machines that make machines at the rate of more than $70 million worth every month. But the production principles remain the same.

The assembly line—the supramachine—has by no means reached its final stage of development. By its very nature, it has a built-in tendency toward further mechanization, toward total automation. This tendency is strangely organic—to many people, frighteningly so, like the groping of some gargantuan creature toward even greater growth—and it hatches new developments of its own, brews fresh situations, raises disturbing issues. What will the supramachine of the future resemble? Something, no doubt, compounded of heat, electricity, energy like the sun's, steel, wires, reels, magnetic tape, computer circuits. The precise answer lies ahead, but we move toward it incontestably, swiftly, as if on bright, soaring, machine-milled wings.

The Beauty
of Machines
at Work

"Machines are worshipped because they are beautiful, and valued because they confer power." So wrote the philosopher Bertrand Russell in 1928. Ever since the Industrial Revolution forever altered the patterns of life and society, mankind's spokesmen, the poets, have praised the beauty of machines. Thus, as early as 1804, William Wordsworth used a machine image to describe a beautiful woman: "And now I see with eye serene, The very pulse of the machine."

No less today, the power and beauty of working machines excite us. The engine of a hot rod rasps into life and a gaggle of teenagers cheers. A jet aircraft whines along a runway and the jetport's observation deck is crammed with spectators watching the takeoff. A construction crane hoists an I beam into place and scores of sidewalk supervisors feel a sense of participation. Here and on the pages that follow are some photographic impressions of machine beauty.

A YOUTH'S PROUD CONSTRUCTION
Lovingly modified and restored, the engine of a hot rod *(opposite)* gleams of chrome, copper and new paint. Built by 18-year-old Bobby Wilner of Port Chester, New York, the car's chassis is a 1930 Ford, the engine a 1958 Oldsmobile. But substitution of parts (including the three Chevy carburetors) makes it a completely new machine; the boy spent $2,500 and nine months creating it.

With a flashing blur of bright color, an old-fashioned spinning machine prepares newly dyed raw silk for the loom at the Fou Wah Weaving Mills in Hong Kong. A hypnotic arrangement of bony arms and heavy iron wheels, the spinner clatters noisily as it reels off continuous threads of finished silk from the skeins on the wheels. The next step for the thread is the loom, where it is woven into rich, brocaded cloth.

An incandescent filament of steel *(above)* is extruded from the furnace at left, making a brilliant display of sparks and color en route to its humble end as ordinary steel pipe. From such machines as this, at a Kaiser Steel Company mill in California, enough pipe is drawn every minute to equip a three-bedroom house.

An arrangement of gears in a Seth Thomas clock of about 1800 is a study of grain and pattern. Except for the brass escapement wheel at top center, all the gears are wood —cherry, ivy or laurel—mounted on a block of oak. Each gear turns on its own axle, meshing with others in a complex interdependence, to move the hands of the clock.

The spidery lines of a 1908
Model T endow the classic car with a gaunt
but functional grace. Mass
production, in which every part down
to the last bolt was designed for
an uncompromisingly utilitarian purpose,
often imposed on machines a
precision that was beautiful in itself.

"CHEWING OUT" A COAL SEAM THE MODERN WAY

Rearing like a hungry dinosaur on the prowl, this orange monster is the mechanical substitute for a coal miner's pickax. As the machine rumbles along under its own electric power, its six rows of teeth rip coal from underground seams with savage efficiency at the rate of five tons per minute. This multiple exposure, which demonstrates the miner's flexibility, shows its hydraulically operated jaws in several "chewing" positions.

MUSIC OF MACHINES
A CENTURY REMOVED

Even when pulled apart for demonstration, a jet engine is a sleek, compact masterpiece of modern design. From the compressor *(left)*, with its 12 sets of whirling blades, to the cavernous chamber of the afterburner at far right, this General Electric J47 turbojet symbolizes motion, power and speed. Assembled, the engine is 19 feet long, tip to tip.

The bristling stubble of brass whiskers on the roller at right comprises the heart of an elegant 19th Century music box. It is a gleaming reflection of the artistry of skilled Swiss workmen. Each spike on the revolving cylinder is precisely placed to play the right note at the right time as the spike revolves past the keyboard at the bottom.

A GLEAMING COLLECTION OF CYLINDERS

In a delicate balance of tension, the heavy cylinders of a paper winder *(below)* spin a "web" of newly made paper at the blurring rate of almost a mile a minute. The large center cylinder keeps the paper taut and flat.

An endless sheet of a versatile plastic
(above) is reflected in two gleaming rollers
as it hums through a finishing machine
in a Du Pont processing plant at Chester Run,
Delaware. The perfect finish of the
chrome-plated cylinders assures a smooth
surface on the plastic. The red bars are a safety
device which stops the machine on contact.

In focusing on a small section of a giant
Harris-Cottrel printing press, the camera
catches here a still life rich in color, form and
texture. The viscous yellow ink is
smoothed in its "fountain" by a spreader
which moves on a geared track. The
glistening drum picks up ink from the fountain
and transfers it to the printing rollers.

BRUTE FORCE AND GEOMETRIC ELEGANCE

Like the mandibles of a predatory beetle,
a timber loader's powerful tongs *(right)*
grapple with two huge logs cut from an
Oregon forest. Air-powered, the tongs are
used for speedy loading of tractor trailers
which truck the timber to nearby
rivers, where they are floated downstream
in great rafts to the sawmills.

With stark geometry of line and angle,
five building cranes *(opposite)* etch their spare
silhouettes against a setting sun. Powerful
applications of lever and pulley, cranes
are among man's oldest complex machines,
dating back to ancient times. The long-legged
structures seen here on a construction site
in Munich can lift 110 tons more than 300 feet.

A FIERY WATERFALL
OF MOLTEN METAL

This infernal scene of monstrous machines
and glaring fire is part of the process
which creates steel, the bones and flesh
of the machine age. At an open-hearth furnace
in Middletown, Ohio, a massive ladle
pours 100 tons of molten pig iron into the
furnace, while the fire's brilliance casts
a workman into satanic silhouette.

The Quickened
World of
Internal Combustion

CONGESTION AND COMBUSTION
Through the medium of the automobile and the airplane, the internal-combustion engine not only ended man's isolation from his fellow man but also drew them together in ways often too close for comfort. In an attempt to unsnarl an evening traffic jam in Los Angeles *(above)*, a helicopter pilot broadcasts news of slow-downs and tie-ups to the hapless groundlings.

NOT LONG AGO a Senate committee studying the impact of technology upon foreign policy issued a report which featured four maps. Placed side by side, they were designed to show, in terms of travel time, the relative size of the world from the sailing-ship days of the 1840s to the jet era of the 1960s. The first map was the size of a man's hand. The last was smaller than the head of a thumbtack.

Two machines, the automobile and the airplane, bear the brunt for this change in the dimensions of human existence. They have, of course, endowed us with unprecedented mobility; during the single year of 1961, for instance, cars and planes took us 606 billion miles within this country alone. They have also given us unprecedented range of choice, allowing us to get involved with more places and people, exposing us to more experiences, stimuli and temptations. In consequence, they have immensely diversified, and complicated, our lives.

The benefits are by now flamboyantly familiar, the detriments subtler but no less apparent. By grace of the jet, a New York executive can breakfast at home, lunch in San Francisco and en route back dine in Chicago, at a table adorned with tulips cut that morning in Amsterdam, on Dover sole caught the day before in the English Channel. A factory hand's wife can almost as easily pick up the week's victuals at a shopping center down the turnpike as at the corner grocery; if her husband is unwilling to commute farther than 15 miles, he can still hold a job within a 700-square-mile area. Yet, along with these magic-carpet wonders, the automobile and the airplane have brought urban sprawl, airport noise, smog, nerve-frazzling traffic jams and the disappearance of about 300,000 acres of land a year beneath concrete roads and runways.

Most of us feel, at times, that machines are forcing a faster pace than we are biologically or psychologically geared to. But we have a way and a history of adapting to mechanisms. To the simple villager, wrote the Frenchman Antoine de Saint-Exupéry, the locomotive was once a smoking iron monster, yet, "What is it today . . . except a humble friend who calls every evening at six?"

So completely are cars and planes the symbols of the flux and tempo of modern life that it is hard to realize that their mechanical ancestry goes back nearly two centuries. The first self-contained, mechanically driven road vehicle was designed in 1769. A steam-powered tractor for pulling cannon, it was a top-heavy, three-wheeled carriage whose boiler awkwardly protruded over the single front wheel; it looked, contemporaries said, like "a whisky still on a wheelbarrow." Its maximum speed was four miles per hour (mph), and at that it had to pause every block or so to build up steam. Its builder, a French Army captain named N. J. Cugnot, ultimately drove the cart into a stone wall. Historians report that he was promptly thrown into jail—the first known traffic offender.

FOUR VITAL STEPS
TO POWER ON THE ROAD

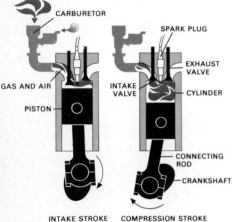

CARBURETOR

SPARK PLUG

EXHAUST VALVE

GAS AND AIR

INTAKE VALVE

CYLINDER

PISTON

CONNECTING ROD

CRANKSHAFT

INTAKE STROKE   COMPRESSION STROKE

The four-stroke-cycle internal-combustion engine is so called because it does its work in a sequence of four strokes of the piston in its cylinder. *First,* the piston moves down, drawing a mixture of air and fuel from the carburetor into the cylinder through the open intake valve. *Second,* the valve closes; the piston moves up, compressing the air-and-fuel vapor to as little as one fourteenth its original volume.

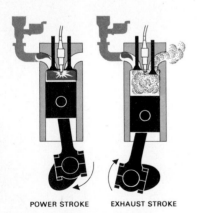

POWER STROKE   EXHAUST STROKE

Third, an electric spark from the spark plug ignites the compressed vapor and causes an explosion which pushes the piston down with a load of several tons. The connecting rod transforms the piston's vertical movement into the crankshaft's rotary motion—at several thousand rpm's. *Fourth,* the exhaust valve opens; the piston moves up again, forcing the burned gases from the cylinder to prepare it for the intake stroke of the next cycle.

There were subsequent steam-propelled road vehicles as picturesque as Cugnot's and even more successful, but steam power was to prove only a temporary expedient for the restless proponents of swifter transportation. A steam engine works by *external* combustion: its fuel—coal, wood, oil—is burned outside the engine. As long ago as the gunpowder experiments of Christian Huygens in the 17th Century, man had conceived of another kind of engine—one that works by *internal* combustion. In it, the fuel would burn or explode inside a closed cylinder tightly fitted with a movable plunger, or piston. The flash of fuel would create hot gases. These would expand, seek a way out. Against the rigid cylinder walls they would push in vain. But the movable piston would give way; they could drive it to the very end of the cylinder, imparting to it their kick, their thrust. And if the piston were connected to a rod, and the rod to a crankshaft and flywheel, then the gases could rotate the shaft, produce motion, turn something, such as a drive pulley. The action would be like that of a Chinese firecracker, except that the cylinder, instead of bursting, would hold fast.

The power in a puzzle

The puzzle and challenge of internal combustion persisted for almost 200 years before it re-attracted attention among mid-19th Century French and German scientists seeking a new prime mover smaller and cheaper to run than a steam engine—"true power units of the people," as Professor Franz Reuleaux put it. These men had much more to work with than did Huygens: improved lathes and other tools for machining moving parts; crude but effective methods of producing sparks by means of electric ignition systems. Moreover, petroleum-industry pioneers such as the Englishman James Young and the Canadian Abraham Gesner had developed new fuels like coal oil and kerosene, which, though originally intended for illumination, promised the quick firing needed for internal combustion.

With such technology and know-how in its favor, an internal-combustion engine finally emerged that would work. As the century progressed, this beautifully machined, compact, explosive creator of power that springs obediently to life at the touch of a switch took on its final form and character. Put it in a carriage and the carriage, all by itself, would carry a man down the road. Cunningly arrange it in something like a glider, set it to twirling a propeller, and the wood-and-canvas wings of the craft would swoop a man up into the air. Eventually this little engine, multiplied by the millions, would furnish Americans with more than 12 billion horsepower a year, and would collapse time and space.

The first significant advance toward this end came in 1860, when the French inventor Étienne Lenoir built a small, single-cylinder internal-combustion engine in which gas was injected first into one end of a horizontal cylinder, then into the other. Electric wire points inside the cylinder received current from a battery and provided sparks that ignited the fuel mixture. The tiny, confined, alternate explosions drove the piston inside the cylinder back and forth like a tennis ball in a fast rally. A rod connected to the piston drove a crank which turned a flywheel. Two years later, another French scientist, Alphonse Beau de Rochas, wrote his now historic analysis of the new engine, in which he established the principle of the "four-stroke" cycle. This principle was applied with notable success, in 1876, by two German mechanics, N. A. Otto, the self-educated son of an innkeeper, and his partner, Eugen Langen. Otto's first four-stroke engine—the "Otto Silent"—burned coal gas. It consumed less than half as much fuel as Lenoir's engine, ran twice as fast and was, quite obviously, the ideal power plant for small mills, machine shops, print shops and other establishments too modest to afford steam power. Soon Otto and Langen had sold 35,000 of their engines to buyers the world over.

The four-stroke cycle (*illustrated on opposite page*) is still the basic operating principle of most internal-combustion engines. In the carburetor —which is essentially an atomizer—gasoline is mixed with air to form an explosive, mistlike spray. This mixture is piped to the cylinder, which is fitted with a movable piston; a rod joins the piston to a crankshaft with flywheel. As the piston moves down in the cylinder, it rotates the shaft; in turn the revolving shaft moves the piston up, down, and up again. Thus the piston's complete cycle consists of four movements (hence "four-stroke cycle"), two up and two down; power is delivered once in every cycle.

Acclaim for a proud father

The man who put the first reliable internal-combustion machine on the road was a German, Karl Benz, who was thereby to earn history's accolade as "father of the automobile." The Benz car, which appeared in 1885, was, like Cugnot's steam-powered contraption, a three-wheeler; but its engine was in the rear, behind the single seat, and the body was light, with large, delicately spoked wheels. The one-cylinder, four-stroke engine burned benzine; at maximum speed it turned its shaft 250 revolutions per minute (rpm's), delivered three fourths of a horsepower, and moved automobile and driver down the road at a stately eight mph. The rear-wheel drive was powered, like a bicycle, by a chain-and-sprocket mechanism. Other features included three that have been standard automotive engineering ever since: electric ignition, a radiator to cool the water that automatically recirculates to keep the cylinder from overheating, and differential gears—a system of gears in the rear axle to accommodate the difference in wheel speeds that occurs when a car turns, even as in a wheeling line of marchers the outside men lengthen and quicken their stride while the inside marchers mark time.

With the Benz model began a steadily stepped-up parade of new cars and new refinements. The next year another German mechanic, Gottlieb Daimler, put on display the first four-wheeled automobile, with a front axle that turned on a central pivot for steering, and with an engine boasting the highest performance to date. The Daimler engine burned oil vapor for fuel and delivered one horsepower for 88 pounds of weight (aluminum engines today deliver one horsepower for less than two pounds); even lighter than the Benz engine, it could run nearly four times as fast—800 to 1,000 rpms.

The impact and excitement of such developments were not lost on an America innately attuned to technological advance. A four-horsepower gasoline buggy—speed 10 mph—was built by the brothers Charles E. and Frank Duryea of Springfield, Massachusetts, and successfully road-tested in 1893. Within two years, a new publication called *The Horseless Age* listed no fewer than 73 experimental-automobile manufacturers around the country—many simply backyard mechanics. The public, however, continued to view the automobile as an expensive toy for the playboy in goggles and linen duster. Then a dour young machinist from the Michigan farm country, Henry Ford, determined to provide a cheap, serviceable, practical car for, as he called it, "the great multitude."

A backdrop of bobolinks

Ford built his first successful automobile in Dearborn in 1896—in the springtime, he later remembered, because he was running it on the road when the bobolinks came to Dearborn that year, and "they always come on April 2." This proto-Ford had a two-cylinder, four-horsepower gasoline engine that ran 60 miles on the three gallons its little tank held. Its wheels were 28-inch, rubber-tired bicycle wheels. Power went from motor to shaft by endless belt, and from shaft to rear wheel by chain-and-sprocket drive.

This elemental contraption held such fascination for Ford, so increasingly did it engross him, that in 1899 he quit his engineering job with the Detroit Edison Company and waded boldly into the automobile business. Nine years later he brought out his famous "universal car," the Model T, a sturdy, four-cylinder, high-riding, practically indestructible car that cost $850. It had absolutely no snob appeal; no one would ever park it proudly in the country-club driveway. On the contrary, it was for wallowing along muddy farm roads, bumping over rocks, putt-putting through the countryside; as Ford himself enthusiastically proclaimed, any man could now "enjoy with his family the blessings of hours of

COUPE, Four passenger, $2250

LIMOUSINE, Seven passenger, $3250

CADILLAC'S CRANKLESS CARRIAGE
Despite the public surge toward the low-cost mass-produced car, the luxury automobile still held its allure—as shown by the prices in the advertisement for the 1912 Cadillac reproduced above. (That year the Ford Model T sold for $590.) But these Cadillacs had an exclusive feature which made them worth every penny to their arm-weary drivers: the first electric self-starter. An immediate hit, this device spelled doom for the ornery hand crank.

pleasure in God's great open spaces." Public resistance to this most personal and soon-to-be most coveted of all man's machines began to crumple. Before Ford discontinued them in 1927, some 15 million Model Ts—"Tin Lizzies," as they were fondly called—rolled off the assembly line and out across America.

Adding stimulus to popular acceptance of the automobile were such improvements as shock absorbers for a more comfortable ride, the use of gears instead of chains to drive the rear wheels and, most important —perhaps the only significant innovation of a basically mechanical nature since the 1890s—the self-starter invented by an electrical engineer, Charles F. Kettering, in 1911.

Epilogue to an accident

Until then, cars were hand-cranked—a hazardous task, since a balky engine would fire too soon, kick back suddenly and spin the crank handle around with vicious, wrist-breaking force. In 1910 a motorist friend of Henry Leland, head of the Cadillac Automobile Company, stopped to help a woman driver stalled on a Detroit bridge. The engine kicked, the crank handle crushed his jaw, and resulting complications caused his death. Deeply affected, Leland put Kettering to work developing an automatic self-starter: an electrical device, powered by the car's own battery, which would "turn over" the engine—to give it its start. Engineers had thought it impossible to build an electric motor big enough to turn over an automobile engine, yet small enough to fit compactly under a hood. But Kettering, with the help of co-workers he liked to call his "barn gang," turned the trick. After several months, he put on a demonstration in his barn-workshop. He pushed a button wired to the new starter of his Cadillac. To the onlookers' amazement, the car roared into operation—without a crank. Self-starters were soon routine equipment.

At the end of World War I, there were 5.5 million motor cars in America—one for every 19 Americans. By the end of the 1920s, there were more than 23 million—about one for every five Americans. By the end of 1963, there were an estimated 82 million, including some 13 million trucks and buses—about one for every two Americans. Moreover, thanks to the ubiquitous farm tractor, the man-hours required to produce 100 bushels of corn dropped—between 1910 and 1960—from 135 to 23; man-hours required to produce 100 bushels of wheat dropped from 106 to 17; man-hours required to produce a bale of cotton dropped from 276 to 77.

Many tractors are powered by the diesel engine, either two-stroke or four-stroke, which has a higher compression ability than the gasoline engine, so that it squeezes more power out of the gallon of fuel. The diesel, which uses a light oil similar to kerosene, is the heavy workhorse among internal-combustion engines; it is widely used in locomotives,

FORD'S FIRST FORD

Henry Ford's original autocar *(below)* was built by hand in 1896 and was little more than a motorized buggy. It had no brakes and could not go in reverse. But Ford was so convinced of its potential that he persevered, and produced racing cars for a while, both to learn the trade and to attract financial backing. Within a dozen years of devising this primitive jalopy, Ford had his epochal Model T in full production.

trucks, buses and all manner of boats from pleasure cruisers to tankers. It also drives electric generators and powers stationary machinery such as air compressors and pumps. This engine was patented in 1892 by Rudolf Diesel, a German engineer whose subsequent career was one of the most intriguing in all technology; a year before World War I, shortly after his engine began to be installed in German submarines, he disappeared off a Channel steamer—a mystery unresolved to this date.

The internal-combustion engine gave man a machine that within a generation increased the number of miles he could reasonably travel in a day from 40 by horse and carriage to 450 by automobile. It also gave him—18 short years after Karl Benz put the first, sputtering motor vehicle on the road—something he had yearned for since the dawn of history: wings. Ungainly, primitive, treacherous wings, to be sure; but wings, nevertheless, that enabled him to fly, to consort with the wind and the birds.

A dilemma of dynamics

For all the changes it has wrought, powered flight in heavier-than-air craft, with man at the controls, was only 60 years old in December 1963. In the beginning there were two major stumbling blocks: lack of a power plant small enough, light enough and at the same time powerful enough to move a heavier-than-air craft; and lack of adequate information about the dynamics of flight—how to guide a plane, turn it, manipulate it in the wind, keep it upright, get it down once it got up.

The Otto Silent internal-combustion engine, with its four-stroke cycle, solved the first problem. Another Otto—Otto Lilienthal—went far toward solving the second. One of a 19th Century breed of stubbornly adventurous spirits who insisted that man could fly, Lilienthal became enthralled with flight while watching the storks of his native Pomerania soar over his house on their unwieldy wings. In 1891, at the age of 43, he began building and flying gliders—monoplanes with curved, ribbed batwings. In the next five years, he made more than 2,000 glides, many from a man-made hill shaped like a cone, so that he could take off downhill in any direction that the wind dictated. These airborne journeys produced invaluable findings on the lifting power of curved surfaces; ultimately these proved that the airstream over the curved upper surface of the wing of a plane must travel farther, hence faster, to meet the airstream below the flat underside of the wing; and that in going faster, the upper airstream becomes thinner, creating powerful suction and thus providing two thirds of the wing's "lift"; the rest comes from the pressure of the lower airstream. Lilienthal paid dearly for his discoveries. On a routine glide in 1896, the wind flipped his glider over and sent it crashing to earth. Lilienthal's back was broken. He died the next day.

MAKING THE WHEELS GO ROUND

Hitching up an engine's horsepower to make it move a car requires a complex mechanical linkage called a "drive train." Essentially, its function is to transmit the crankshaft's rotary motion to the rear of the car and "bend" it at right angles to turn the back wheels, which in almost all cars do the work of driving (the front wheels more or less go along for the ride). The drive shaft carries the power back to the differential, whose gears turn the axles and wheels. The two other major parts of the drive train, the clutch and transmission, function to vary the speed and the turning direction of the drive shaft and wheels.

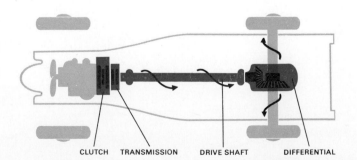

CLUTCH   TRANSMISSION   DRIVE SHAFT   DIFFERENTIAL

Other pioneers kept his work alive. Foremost among them, in America, were Octave Chanute, a French-born civil engineer, and Professor S. P. Langley, an astronomer and secretary of the Smithsonian Institution. In the mid-1890s Chanute built many gliders and, with the help of his pilot, A. M. Herring, tested them above the windy dunes along Lake Michigan's south shore. Through his knowledge of bridge-building he was able to design structural strength into his flying models; he experimented with multiwinged craft—three- and even five-deckers—before concluding that the two-winged craft, or biplane, was, at this stage of the game, the safest and most maneuverable.

Langley's involvement with aircraft was relatively brief and, for himself, a crushing disappointment. He too began his experiments in the 1890s, building models powered first with wide rubber bands, later with tiny steam engines. Some of his planes had wingspreads of 16 feet, and flew prettily out over the Potomac from the testing ground on the riverbank. Langley became convinced that gasoline engines were the means to powered flight. In 1898, he received encouragement of a sort seldom bestowed upon the inventive: Congress itself granted him $50,000 to build a flying machine. After successful tests with a gasoline-powered model—first of its kind ever flown—he constructed a full-sized monoplane powered by a five-cylinder, 53-horsepower motor whose chain-and-sprocket drive turned two propellers. Before a corps of skeptical Washington reporters in early October 1903, workmen mounted Langley's aircraft on a catapult atop his Potomac River houseboat. His assistant, Charles M. Manly, sat strapped at the controls. The motor, which Manly had built, roared. A mechanic gave the signal. The intricate wings tilted off the edge of the houseboat roof, and the craft, propellers thrashing, clattered noisily into the river.

History in 12 seconds

Convinced that the machine had somehow tangled in the launching gear, Langley repaired it and, on December 8, made another attempt. Again the craft tumbled dolefully into the river. Its despairing inventor, lampooned and jeered by most of the nation's press, gave up. Nine days later, on the lonely beach at Kitty Hawk, North Carolina, the brothers Wilbur and Orville Wright succeeded where Langley and everyone else had failed. Their gasoline-powered plane, with Orville at the controls, lurched up into the wind, staggered through the air for 12 seconds, flew 120 feet, then settled slowly back onto the sand.

Later the Wrights dated their obsession with flying back to the day in 1878 when their father had brought home a toy helicopter. In their twenties they had pored over books and papers by Lilienthal, Chanute and Langley. They had proceeded methodically, building a small wind tunnel six feet long and 16 inches square, testing in it more than 200 varieties of wing surfaces. They taught themselves what others had learned: that cambered, or curved, aircraft wings, angled up slightly, would sustain an aircraft—that is, the pressure of air against these wings would sustain it, just as the pressure of air against the inclined face of a kite sustains it. Then, if an engine-mounted propeller with pitched, or angled, blades were attached to the wings and spun around rapidly like an electric fan, it would drive a column of air backward; the propeller would thus push itself forward and take the sustained plane with it.

But one also had to know how to turn, how to stabilize the craft. And so the Wrights studied birds. They saw how buzzards, for instance, kept their balance when one wing dropped by twisting the dropped wing; the increased pressure on the wing stabilized them, leveled them off. The two men proved this out in tests with gliders equipped with wing tips they could twist, or warp, from the ground by means of control wires. A second triumph was the linking of the warping controls with those that governed a rear, movable rudder and, through the rudder, turned the craft to the left or right. The Wrights had already fitted the craft with an elevator, a movable surface that would make it go up or down; now, by means of the synchronized wing and rudder controls, they could turn the craft smoothly, tilting the wings in a graceful bank, and then, just as smoothly, restore horizontal balance.

There was no opportunity to fly like this that first day, December 17, 1903, at Kitty Hawk. The craft was a biplane, with wooden frame and canvas wings. Its four-cylinder, 12-horsepower engine drove two propellers, mounted behind the wings, by the old chain-and-sprocket drive. It made four flights against a stiff head wind that historic morning, the longest lasting 59 seconds and traveling 852 feet.

Instruments of the inevitable

Two years later, the Wrights, in an aircraft powered by a 24-horsepower engine, flew 24 miles in 38 minutes. In 1908, Wilbur flew 76 miles without touching earth. In the next memorable year Louis Blériot took off from French soil in his monoplane and flew across the English Channel to Dover in 37 minutes—the first international plane flight. By the end of World War I, which established the airplane as a new and revolutionary weapon, machines could fly more than 150 mph, climb to an altitude of 25,000 feet and range nonstop for 1,000 miles. Lindbergh's solo conquest of the Atlantic in the *Spirit of St. Louis* in May 1927 was a magnificent triumph of individuality. But, looking back, we can see that he and his plane were instruments of the inevitable. After Kitty Hawk, it was bound to happen. The only question was when.

As aircraft evolved, they lost their early look of ponderous and un-

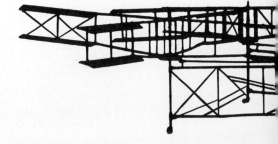

THE WORLD'S FIRST WHIRLYBIRD
In 1907, less than four years after the Wrights' first flight, a French engineer, Louis Bréguet, actually got off the ground in this extraordinary contraption—the first helicopter. Called *Gyroplane #1*, it had four double-deck, 26-foot rotors driven by a 45-hp engine. Bréguet got five feet up in the air, but could not manage horizontal flight and had to be hauled hither and yon by assistants on the ground.

gainly insects. They became simpler, more functional. Fuselage and single cambered wing took on pure, natural lines, like those of a sea-shell, a fish, a wave-polished stone. The planes became more efficient, capable of faster speeds and higher altitudes. And therein lay a problem, as well as the next great advance in aeronautics. For the internal-combustion engine was not up to the new speeds and altitudes. An even more powerful prime mover was in order: jet propulsion.

The first jet-propulsion engine—the turbojet—was patented in 1930 by Group Captain Frank Whittle of the British Royal Air Force. But while Britain debated its usefulness, German aircraft engineers pushed its development. In 1939, five days before the Nazis invaded Poland, their test pilots flew the world's first turbojet airplane, a Heinkel He 178. British and American models appeared in the skies in subsequent years of the war. Representing an enormous advance in military aircraft, the jet plane then revolutionized postwar commercial aviation. A man could now board a plane at Idlewild Airport in New York and be in Honolulu in half the time the crack Twentieth Century Limited would have taken to get him to Chicago three decades earlier.

Echoes of a toy balloon

The turbojet engine derives its name from the turbine—a bladed wheel which functions like a small, multiwinged windmill—placed at the back of the combustion chamber. The engine has no propeller. It is called a "reaction" engine—like Hero's *aeolipile* two millennia earlier—because, as it shoots a continuous blast of hot gases rearward, it reacts by moving forward itself. The effect is the same as when a child inflates a toy balloon, holds its stem, then lets go; air rushing out of the stem propels the balloon through the air.

A masterpiece of simplicity, the turbojet engine is encased in what is essentially a large hollow tube; it voraciously sucks air in at the front end, compresses it, then burns fuel in it. The hot gases expand and rush out of the back of the tube. The engine has but one moving part: a drive shaft extending through its center from front to back. At the front end is the turbocompressor, or supercharger. This draws in a constant stream of air and compresses it—squeezes it, raising its temperature as in the gasoline engine—by forcing it through a metal maze consisting of alternately fixed and revolving rows of tiny blades. The stream of hot, compressed air then passes into a combustion chamber. An injector sprays a kerosene-like fuel through it (an electric starter has begun the process by igniting the fuel in the first stage of operation). The fuel burns constantly, like a blowtorch, producing hot, high-pressure gases. As they expand, seeking a way out through the rear of the combustion chamber, they strike the turbine and spin it at high speed. Rushing past

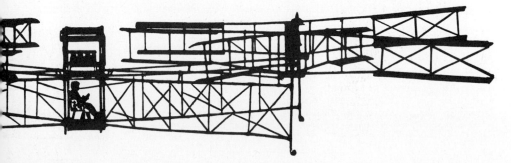

or through the turbine, they encounter a nozzlelike, rear-exhaust opening which raises their velocity and concentrates their force. They shoot out the end at terrific speed, delivering a kick or thrust that in the largest engines is equivalent to 75,000 horsepower.

Rockets? They are also reaction engines, like enormous gun barrels —propelled, as are turbojets, by hot, high-pressure gases rushing out their afterend. There is, however, an important difference. The jet plane depends on oxygen in the earth's atmosphere, so cannot fly beyond the limits of the atmosphere. A rocket, on the other hand, carries oxygen with it, usually in the form of liquid oxygen, or LOX. For this reason it is the first engine—the first machine—that is not earthbound. As recently as 1946, rockets were experimental devices fuming up into the hot blue sky over White Sands in New Mexico. Today they can propel a nuclear warhead 6,000 miles in 35 minutes. They can send an astronaut into orbit around the earth at 17,500 mph. They have inspired a new technology of space. They have created a multibillion-dollar industry, which, in the number of its workers and the investment it represents, may by 1970 far exceed all our automotive industries combined.

Man's wings were first made of linen or canvas, then of metal. Now they are fashioned of white flame, and have borne him off farther than ever from home.

Today's Inventor, Genius in Harness

Modern inventors are a far remove from the popular image of their predecessors —as distant, say, as the electronic computer is from Edison's light bulb. En route from bulb to computer they have put a sizable dent in the picture of the inventor as a solitary crackpot, oblivious to food, dress and the amenities. Although independents still exist, most inventors today work as part of a team in laboratories, maintained at high cost by government or private industry. They are sometimes called captive inventors, but they are well paid for their bondage, and they are likely to favor natural-shoulder suits and haute cuisine. Still, the old image haunts them, like the hall portrait of a remote ancestor. "Don't call me an inventor," says Scott Rethorst (*opposite*). "An inventor is a nut. I'd rather be considered a scientist." On the following pages LIFE photographer Alfred Eisenstaedt portrays some of today's restlessly imaginative scientist-inventors.

A RADICAL CONCEPT IN TRAVEL
Scott Rethorst of Pasadena's Vehicle Research Corporation holds a model of *Columbia*, a craft which is designed to move on a cushion of air blown downward at high pressure. Rethorst is an advocate of the modern concept of group research, and employs a staff of 40. But his shop, an aged building behind an advertising billboard, is reminiscent of an oldtime inventor's shack.

FLEXIBLE WINGS FOR MANY USES

Francis M. Rogallo, a NASA scientist at the Langley Research Center in Hampton, Virginia, displays models of flexible wings which may have many military uses. The concept was developed at home, on weekends. Rogallo and his wife made one model from discarded curtains. The government took up Rogallo's ideas in 1958 and has invested nearly $30 million.

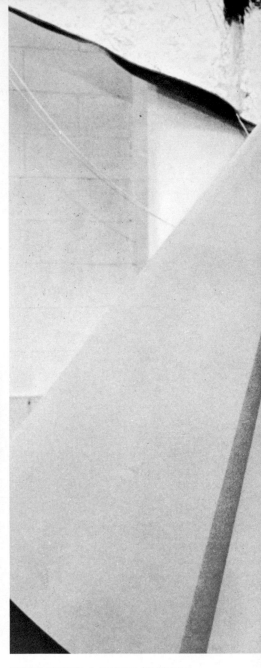

MISSILE WITH A SINGLE PURPOSE

Dr. William B. McLean, the technical director of the U.S. Naval Ordnance Test Station at China Lake, California, stands behind the guidance unit of the Sidewinder, an astonishingly accurate air-to-air missile. McLean, an inventor since childhood, spent three years simply thinking about how to create the missile. He feels that "it's important not to start too fast."

The Rewards of Inspiration amid Bureaucracy

Inventors in the direct employ of the government make up a small minority of their profession. Yet the federal government is actively concerned with the development of new inventions, and is involved in a program to stimulate their creation. In fiscal 1963, Washington picked up a research tab amounting to about $11 billion. Of this sum, about $8.5 billion was handed out to private industry and universities; a relatively small contribution of $2.5 billion went to federal facilities.

Despite this imbalance, government inventors have made major contributions, especially in the defense and space fields. Often these are achieved in the face of problems normally out of an inventor's ken but indigenous to bureaucracy. "A really novel invention can be tremendously upsetting to a large organization," the

Navy's Dr. William B. McLean (left), inventor of the Sidewinder guided missile, has said. "[It] naturally develops mechanisms to protect itself from such disturbances." And these mechanisms become a spaghetti-like mass of red tape designed to discourage all but the most stubborn.

Nevertheless, many federal inventors have persisted successfully—notably McLean and Francis M. Rogallo (above) of NASA. McLean has received a $25,000 prize for his work. In addition, a government ruling permits McLean to collect foreign royalties and he earns an income from the missile's production for NATO in West Germany. Rogallo invented a totally flexible wing which may be used for recovery of space vehicles and has potential applications for air cargo delivery. In 1963, NASA awarded him a $35,000 prize.

The Gray Flannel Inventor's Freedom to Create

The inventor as an organization man is a seeming contradiction. No one understands this better than two groups: the inventors who work for large corporations and, fortunately, their bosses. Inventors on the payrolls of the nation's major companies enjoy a vast freedom to create. It is, in fact, the large companies which can best afford to allow individual inventors the time and research funds to pursue an idea until it fails or succeeds. "Only individuals get ideas. Committees don't get them," says Joseph B. Bidwell *(right)*, head of the Engineering Mechanics Department of General Motors' Research Laboratories. "But this is really not the end of things. After the idea stage there's a tremendous amount of development which, from a practical standpoint, is just as significant as the invention."

It is precisely this wedding of individual initiative and team development that makes industrial research so appealing to many of today's inventors. It also helps account for the high rate of corporate invention. Of the 49,000 patents issued by the U.S. Patent Office in 1961, some 34,000 —or 69 per cent—were assigned to corporations. In 1901 the figure was 18.2 per cent. To achieve these impressive heights, corporations in fiscal 1963 spent more than $4.7 billion of their own and approximately $7.5 billion of government financing for research and development.

TAPE FOR A PUSH-BUTTON LIBRARY
Dr. William E. Glenn of GE's Research Laboratory in Schenectady, New York, holds a reel of his thermoplastic tape. As well as recording sound, the three-layered tape records visual images in color or black and white without any processing—by electronically produced wrinkles on the tape. It could record the 24-volume *Encyclopaedia Britannica* on one small spool.

CAR WITHOUT A STEERING WHEEL
Joseph B. Bidwell lounges in the driver's seat
of Firebird III, GM's experimental car, to which
he contributed the "unicontrol" system—a single control stick to steer, accelerate and brake
the car—and a front and rear suspension which
reduces pitching motion. Like so many ideas,
these may never get beyond the testing stage
before they are superseded by improvements.

Independents:
The Ever-hopeful
Thousands

At a time when big budgets and big organizations seem almost to be prerequisites for invention, it is noteworthy that hope still springs eternal in the creative minds of independent inventors. In 1951, Sinclair Oil invited inventive Americans to submit ideas for possible development. The company received 50,000 suggestions in three years. The fact that few were usable is not necessarily significant; independent inventors rarely make original contributions in the chemical field. Of patents awarded to individuals in recent years, only 7 per cent have been in chemistry; 52 per cent have been for mechanical and electrical ideas.

When Philadelphia's station WCAU-TV started a program called "The Big Idea" to give inventors a chance to demonstrate their brain children, 36,000 people responded. In six and a half years, 1,600 inventors went on the air. More than 400 sold their inventions, receiving from a few thousand dollars to—in three cases—more than a million. Freelance inventors send 1,000 ideas a month to the National Inventors Council, a branch of the Department of Commerce which serves as a clearinghouse for inventions sought by the government. Only about 35 a month are considered worthy of referral to the proper government agency.

Despite their low batting average, independent inventors continue to swing for the elusive fame and fortune which traditionally accrue to the creator of a successful invention. Their inspiration comes from, among others, the three men and one woman on these pages. These four are inventors who have been successful on their own. And they prove that the successful independent inventor can still reap fame—and amass a goodly fortune.

SPEEDING UP PIECEWORK
Richard Walton displays his newest invention, a still-unnamed machine which can pick up a single piece of textile material from a stack of cut pieces, an operation now done by hand. Commercial licensing of this and other machines for the textile trade brings Walton an annual income in six figures, which supports further research in his basement workshop in Boston.

AUTOMATION FOR THE POST OFFICE
Jacob Rabinow inspects his automatic mail facer and canceler, which he developed under contract for the Post Office. Using a scanner to determine the location of each envelope's stamp, the machine flips the envelope into position and cancels the stamp. Rabinow left his $9,200-a-year government job to work for himself and now employs 80 in his Rockville, Maryland, plant.

IMPROVEMENTS FOR DAILY LIFE
Charles Hollerith of Jackson, Michigan, with 77 patents to his credit, stands behind a muffler, muffler tube, brake and wheel of his design. Hollerith has also invented a power drive for lawn mowers, a control console to eliminate the cords on electric cooking utensils, a dishwasher, a magnetic chase to speed up printing and the first concealed, inside hood latch for automobiles.

CONTAINER FOR SENSITIVE GOODS
Dr. Maria Telkes holds a beakerful of a chemical she synthesized. The compound derives from her work in solar heating and maintains a uniform temperature (without electricity) for five days in the container used to ship guidance systems of the Polaris missile. The containers are made at the Cryo-Therm company of Fogelsville, Pennsylvania, where she directs research.

117

POWER TOOLS FOR HOBBYISTS

Hans Goldschmidt smiles from behind the Shop-smith, the multipurpose power tool which has grossed above $90 million. He invented it after the war and started production on a capital of $20,000. Sales zoomed in the wake of the do-it-yourself fad. Goldschmidt sold his company in 1958 and now operates a freelance toy and game design company in Menlo Park, California.

DRY COPYING FOR OFFICES

Chester Carlson pauses at a busy point in the Webster, New York, plant of the Xerox Corporation, where the machines which use his copying process are manufactured. Xerography was the first fast, efficient and dry copying process available to business firms. Carlson has been amply rewarded: by mid-1963, he had earned more than $30 million from his invention.

Successful Inventing, a Blend of Luck, Timing and Shrewd Business

Thomas Edison once said, "I have made very little profit from my inventions. . . . Counting the expense of experimenting and fighting for my claims in court, these patents have cost me more than they have returned me in royalties. I have made money through the introduction and sale of my products as a manufacturer." With few exceptions, most inventors who have made money in recent years would agree wholeheartedly with Edison's words. The invention itself is almost invariably only a first step to financial success. Some inventors with a business sense exploit their own products. Many must turn to others for help. All agree that proper marketing plus timing and luck are essential.

The experience of Chester Carlson *(below)* proves the point. Carlson invented the copying process known as xerography, but then had to search until he found a small, daring company—which has since become the Xerox Corporation—to bring it on the market. And Xerox might not have made it if the need for a fast and inexpensive dry copying process had not existed. On the other hand, Carlson once gave up an idea for what eventually became the ball-point pen, long before it was marketed, because he did not think it would work.

HELICOPTERS FOR TRAILERS

Igor Sikorsky, one of the deans of American aviation, stands before the Skycrane, a helicopter capable of carrying a loaded truck trailer. Sikorsky, a Russian émigré, designed and developed many types of airplanes while perfecting his helicopter. He sold his own company to United Aircraft, where as engineering chief he produced his first operable helicopter in 1939.

119

Computer and Transistor, Electronic Genii Shaping Our Future

The extent to which a major invention changes our lives can probably never be fully measured. The 60 million television sets now in American homes, compared to the 5,000 in 1946 or some 200,000 in 1948, do not even begin to indicate the full impact of the ubiquitous instrument on American life.

Yet, pervasive as television's influence has been, its ability to touch and affect our lives may be overshadowed in the future, if it has not been already, by the postwar period's two greatest inventions —the electronic computer and the transistor. The transistor, which has replaced the vacuum tube in many instances but is much smaller, more reliable and more durable, has helped make space exploration a reality and hundreds of new products possible.

There are now more than 15,500 computers at work for U.S. business and government, and another 7,800 on order. Yet, computer technology is still in its infancy.

ELECTRONIC BRAINS FOR INDUSTRY
Dr. John W. Mauchly *(left)* and J. Presper Eckert stand behind the console of Univac I, an early model of their high-speed electronic computer. A firm they founded was sold to Sperry Rand, where Eckert is now a vice president; Mauchly runs a consulting firm in Fort Washington, Pennsylvania. Once asked, "Do machines think?" Mauchly replied, "I compute so."

TINY SPUR TO THE SPACE AGE
Dr. William Schockley holds a transistor for which he won (along with W. H. Brattain and John Bardeen) the Nobel Prize as co-inventor. Schockley, a director of research and development for Clevite Corporation in Palo Alto, foresees the transistor's greatest role as part of the computer, to take over "the menial mental jobs of man-ordering, searching, retrieving."

6

Electrical Servants of Everyman

TEN YEARS FROM NOW, experts on such matters predict, the average American home will have at its disposal the services of more than 75 separate and distinct electrical appliances—almost quadruple the number in common use a generation ago. The average American, exercising his inalienable right to be cantankerous, may or may not find every last one of these devices, gadgets or thingumabobs conducive to his particular way of life. But however many he may choose to pass up, he will be bucking a national trend. Machines have long since come into the home to stay, forging an intimacy with their individual owners that is unique in technological history.

Electricity has personalized the machine by supplying man with his own private horsepower at his own private hearthside. Electric motors no bigger than matchboxes run our shaving machines; motors the size of tennis balls run our mixers, blenders and hair dryers; larger motors run our fans, refrigerators, furnaces and vacuum cleaners. Human comfort and convenience hinge on machines powered by electricity as they never hinged on machines powered by water or steam. There is a curious irony in this. Whereas water and steam are reassuringly familiar, electricity—which has done so much more to make man beholden to the machine—is also much more alien to him. Hiding in a wire, living a secret life in the wall, it is silent, unseen, quickly obedient if treated with respect, yet dangerous and intractable if handled without care.

Even as it has mechanized the home, this enigmatic fount of energy has wrought fundamental and irrevocable social and economic change throughout the land:

• Because electricity can be "piped," through wires, almost anywhere—borne by high-tension lines across mountains, deserts and all manner of natural obstacles—factories no longer need be situated hard by their sources of power. As a result, they have been able, particularly in lighter industries, to relocate at will, resettling entire armies of workers in the less noisome suburbs of Boston and New York, the more relaxed climes of California and the Southwest.

• Within the factory itself, compact electric motors, delivering energy cleanly and quietly, have done away with the clamorous maze of shafts, pulleys and belts that used to drive machinery.

• Electricity has led to a whole new breed of machines—the electronic variety—of which television and computers are but two samples. We shall consider such machines in detail in the next chapters; suffice it to say here that their full implications are still to be understood. They are machines that many fear, but machines, nonetheless, that we could not and would not banish. In a large sense, they spell much of the difference between yesterday and tomorrow, between simpler eras gone by and the age of automation, Mach VI and moon shots.

FACETS OF A FOUNTAINHEAD
Its glass and ceramic insulators resplendently aloft, the huge power plant *(left)* at Parker Dam on the Colorado River furnishes a healthy share of the nation's electric resources. The silent strength of electricity, sent through wires over distances impossible for water or steam power, has given new mobility to America's industry and new comforts and conveniences to its citizenry.

The origins of these latter-day marvels and their predecessors go back several centuries; as with so many major breakthroughs in scientific knowledge, their roots lay in a random experiment. In this instance the innocuous subject was a dissected frog, the experimenter an 18th Century Italian professor of anatomy, Luigi Galvani, in whose honor we have the word "galvanize"—to stimulate by current. Pursuing his anatomical researches one day in the 1780s, Galvani hung a dissected frog by its legs on two brass hooks against an iron trellis. Suddenly he noticed the legs twitching, and concluded that "animal electricity" had contracted the leg muscles. As it turned out, he was wrong; nevertheless what he had done would make him and his frog immortal.

Long before the Christian era men had known of the magnetic properties of lodestones—fragments of an iron ore called magnetite. By the 12th Century they had devised the magnetic compass; still later they discovered the existence of the earth's magnetic poles. They were also aware of static electricity, the kind generated by feet scuffing across a carpeted room. Now Galvani, although he did not realize it, had come upon another form of electricity: one that traveled in a continuous current, that would flow along a wire like water through a pipe—that would one day light a lamp and drive a machine.

Galvani's finding inspired another Italian, the physicist Alessandro Volta, to conduct some experiments of his own. Soon Volta uncovered the real explanation of why the frog's legs twitched: two dissimilar metals, together with moisture (in Galvani's test, the brass of the hooks, the iron of the trellis and the moist tissues of the frog's legs), produced electricity when in contact with each other. This electricity, passing as a current from the hook, through the frog, through the fence and back to the hook, stimulated the nerves of the frog's legs, causing them to twitch. Volta thereupon made his own massive contribution to science: he fashioned a simple device for creating electrical current.

A potent pile of poker chips

As first described by Volta in 1800, his battery, or "voltaic pile," as it became known, resembled a stack of good-sized poker chips—disks made of three materials: zinc, copper, and brine-soaked cardboard. They were arranged in sequence, starting at the bottom of the stack: copper, zinc, cardboard, copper, zinc, cardboard and so on. The copper and zinc provided the two dissimilar metals; the brine in the cardboard provided the conducting fluid. When Volta simultaneously touched the bottom copper disk and the top zinc disk, he received an electric shock.

Essentially, the voltaic pile was a prime mover—without moving parts —for transforming chemical energy into electricity. The two different metals served as "electrodes," or oppositely charged poles; the brine

A NEW AGE OF ABUNDANCE AND ITS MASTER BUILDER

EARLY MODEL OF A DYNAMO

One of the brightest luminaries of English science, Michael Faraday *(above)* pointed the way to today's gigantic exploitation of electric power by building a machine to produce electricity from magnetism. It consisted of a 12-inch copper disk, mounted on an axle, between the poles of a magnet. When the disk was rotated through the magnetic field, an electric current was generated and fed through the connecting wires.

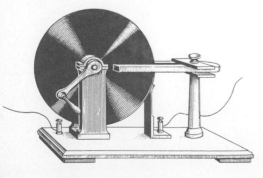

served as an "electrolyte," or conducting fluid. The zinc, reacting with the brine, released a stream of electrons, atomic particles that form an electric current. The current left the zinc electrode, flowed through the brine to the copper electrode, then completed the circuit by returning through Volta himself (later through a wire) to the zinc electrode.

Volta's pile launched a widespread inquiry into the character and crotchets of electricity. Men looked with deepened fascination on this strange power that could either flash in Jovian streaks across the sky or set a delicate needle to quivering, as a leaf in the wind. They pondered it and played with it; they talked and wrote about it, and never stopped trying to fathom it. Within three decades of Volta's triumph, three primary discoveries brought electrically powered machines within reach. The discoverers formed a diverse group—a professor, a onetime bookbinder, a Frenchman felicitously named Hippolyte Pixii, and an apprentice actor turned schoolteacher.

The wayward compass

The professor was Hans Christian Oersted, a Danish physicist. In the spring of 1820, while lecturing to a class at the University of Copenhagen, Oersted happened to push a magnetic compass under a live electric wire. Ordinarily the needle of the compass, in obedience to the pull of the earth's magnetic poles, would point north; this time, following a pull obviously stronger, the needle veered and swung into line at right angles to the wire. Oersted thereby confirmed a fact he had long pursued in his researches: that a wire carrying an electric current produced a force that acted like a magnet. He had discovered, in a word, electromagnetism.

The ex-bookbinder was a young Englishman, Michael Faraday, whose passion for science had won for him a post in London as a laboratory assistant at the thriving research center known as the Royal Institution. If electricity could produce magnetism, Faraday asked himself, was it possible that magnetism could produce electricity? The answer, excitingly affirmative, appeared in a machine devised by Faraday in 1831 (*opposite*). Crude as it was, this contrivance represented the world's first dynamo—from the Greek *dynamis*, power—the first machine to generate current electricity, hence the priceless blueprint to the vast electric power resources of the modern age.

Across the Channel a few months after Faraday's achievement, Pixii, a man of redoubtable engineering and technical skills, constructed a practicable generator (*right*) capable of an output of current far surpassing that of Faraday's machine in strength and steadfastness.

The fourth discoverer was an American, Joseph Henry, whose contribution to technology came about, in an odd way, through the world of books. As a 10-year-old in upstate New York, Henry chased a rabbit

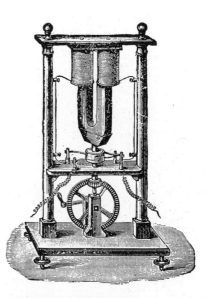

A FRENCH REFINEMENT
The first useful electric generator *(above)*—devised by Hippolyte Pixii, a French instrument maker—considerably improved on Faraday's model *(opposite)*. A magnet was set on end like a "U" beneath two coils of wire. A shaft connected the magnet to geared wheels and to a hand crank which spun the magnet on its axis. The rapidly alternating magnetic field produced a voltage stronger and steadier than that of Faraday's dynamo.

through a gap in the wall of the village church and stumbled upon a cache of novels. Their blood-and-thunder contents fired him into an early apprenticeship with a theatrical company in Albany. While thus engaged, he fell ill, and during a siege in bed chanced to read a popular book on science. Henry forthwith enrolled at Albany Academy, piled up an impressive record as a student, and soon embarked on a teaching career which ultimately returned him to the Academy as a professor of mathematics. There, in 1829, he invented the forerunner of today's powerful electromagnets: a horseshoe-shaped bar of iron, tightly wrapped with insulated wire, which, when charged with electric current, magnetized the iron. By 1831—the year Faraday built his dynamo—Henry had so improved his invention that it was capable of lifting fully a ton of metal.

A matter of magnets and coils

Intensely practical men bent to the task of putting all these discoveries to intensely practical use. By shifting the relative positions of magnets and current-charged coils into various arrangements, they were able to build small motors that would produce rotary motion. In 1837, Thomas Davenport, a Vermont blacksmith, devised the first electric motor to drive industrial machines—in this instance, his own iron and steel drills, his wood-turning lathe. Seven years later, another American, Samuel F. B. Morse, tapped out the first historic message on his new electromagnetic telegraph, ushering in instantaneous communication. In 1876, a Belgian electrical engineer named Zénobe Théophile Gramme designed a dynamo which, because of its convenient size and its ability to produce a genuinely continuous current, was the first to be widely sold. Also in 1876, in Boston, Alexander Graham Bell transmitted the sound of the human voice over a wire by electromagnetic means; by late 1877, more than 9,000 of his telephones were in use in the United States.

A year later Thomas Alva Edison, the electrical wizard of Menlo Park, New Jersey, buckled down to the crowning achievements of his extraordinary career—the development of a workable incandescent lamp and the establishment of the central-station system of distributing electricity for light and power.

The incandescent lamp operates on a deceptively simple principle. When a substance resists the passage of an electric current, heat is generated. When the substance becomes white-hot, it glows, or incandesces, throwing off light. Adapting electricity to light man's lamps was an idea by no means original with Edison. As far back as the first decade of the 19th Century the celebrated Sir Humphry Davy, in the wake of his researches into electrochemistry, had invented the carbon arc light—a light from the spark, or arc, formed in the passage of an electric current between two adjacent rods of carbon. Sir Humphry's only source of

FORERUNNER OF GIANTS
Electric light and the name of Thomas Edison are synonymous in most minds, but many American cities enjoyed the benefits of such lighting even before Edison's incandescent lamp. Although harsher and more glaring, the arc lamp—notably a model invented by Charles Brush—attracted hosts of industrial users, necessitating power plants like the one above, itself hung with arc lamps *(rectangles at top)* and run by tiny dynamos *(foreground)*.

126

current had been the voltaic cell; it took 2,000 of them to produce one sputtering arc. But by the 1870s, thanks to the improvement of the electric generator, a number of lighthouses, public buildings and city squares on both sides of the Atlantic blazed after dark with overhead arc lights. Their dazzling glare was admirably suited to the Capitol dome in Washington, but it was hardly the cozy glow a family wanted in its parlor. No, wrote Edison, it was too big, too bright. "What we wished for was little lights, and a distribution of them to people's houses in a manner similar to gas."

Incandescent lamps had already been developed with limited success in the 1850s by the English chemist Joseph (later Sir Joseph) Swan. Swan and Edison, in fact, took the same tack: the filament lamp, in which passage of electricity through a piece of carbon or resistant wire heated the carbon or wire to incandescence. To keep the filament from oxidizing and disintegrating, Swan placed it in a vacuum—a glass bulb with the air pumped out.

While he continued to work on his lamp in England, across the ocean Edison and his backers formed the Edison Electric Light Company and pushed ahead. Immediately they ran into trouble with the filament. Although the oxidizing problem had been solved, the problem of fusing remained. Every metal they tried for the filament melted under the strength of current they wanted to use. Pondering the matter in his laboratory one day, Edison idly fingered a mixture of tar and lampblack carbon that an assistant had left on his table. He rolled it until it formed a thin thread. Suddenly he examined the thread more closely. On a hunch, he made another thread like it, fitted it into a bulb and turned on the current. The light it gave was bright and beautiful, but quickly burned out. Ultimately he decided that carbon was indeed the answer—but a more durable form of carbon. In an inspired moment, he thought of trying cotton thread, charred to a carbon filament.

Stamina in a light bulb

To mold one perfect, unbroken specimen and wire it into a bulb took nearly three days, but the lamp shed a soft, warm glow. "The problem was solved," he wrote, "if the filament would last. The day was—let me see—October 21, 1879. We sat and looked, and the lamp continued to burn. . . . It lasted about 45 hours, and then I said, 'If it will burn that number of hours now, I know I can make it burn a hundred.'"

Edison, however, was still unsatisfied. To carbonize a flimsy piece of thread and fix it in a bulb without a break was an excruciating task. "Somewhere in God's mighty workshop," he declared, "there is a dense woody growth with fibers almost geometrically parallel and with practically no pith, from which excellent strands can be cut." After testing

INGREDIENTS OF A BULB

Seeking a suitable material for the filament of his brave new lamp, Edison tried charred cardboard. This carbonizing process shrank the filament (above, Figure 1) from its size as molded (2). The resulting carbon "horseshoe" —as Edison workers called it—was placed between two platinum vises (a) inside a glass vacuum bulb (3). Screwed into a socket (4) and with the current turned on (b), the lamp could glow as brightly as 8 to 10 gas jets.

NEW WONDER IN OLD MANHATTAN

After devising his incandescent lamp, Edison built a central station to furnish its light—and electric power—to a whole area. At its peak in 1884, his pioneer Pearl Street station in New York serviced 10,164 lamps and 508 customers. Its steam engines drove six jumbo dynamos (above) weighing 62,000 pounds each. The operation went so well that by 1885 most U.S. electric companies were converting to incandescent lighting.

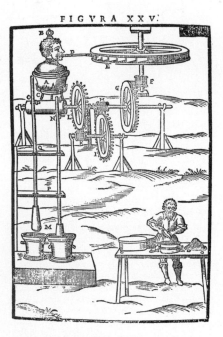

STEAM TURBINE ITALIAN-STYLE
History fails to record that the contraption above was ever actually attempted, but this engraving of it in a 17th Century tome by the Italian architect Giovanni Branca is the earliest pictorial evidence that the steam-turbine concept is a venerable one. A bronze boiler shaped like a human head *(B)* spews steam against a bladed wheel *(E)*, which turns a series of gears *(G, L, I)*, which move a pair of pounding pestles up and down in mortars *(M)*.

thousands of materials secured the world over, he found what he sought —in a strip of bamboo from a Japanese fan. (Today's filaments, far less flimsy, are made of tungsten, a metal which takes high temperatures.)

On New Year's Eve, 1880, Edison strung half a hundred electric bulbs in and around his laboratory at Menlo Park and invited the public to have a look. Visitors flocked by the thousands to gape at the white magic. One journalist, tongue in cheek, reported that the evening star was actually not the planet Venus but one of Edison's lamps, dangling from an invisible balloon. His story drew letters from readers across several states, demanding to know how the inventor got his light up in the sky.

A fruitful underground dig

But what good were the lamps if they could not light offices, stores, shops and homes without a generator on the spot? Edison's answer was his next masterstroke: the electric current would be distributed to an entire area from a centrally located generating station. With the approval of the city of New York, he selected a district in lower Manhattan and went to work. His men spent two years digging trenches and installing the 14 miles of underground conduits required to power the 400 lamps of his initial 85 customers. He started a lamp factory, designed the fixtures and invented a meter to measure each customer's use of current. He also ordered six high-speed, steam-powered dynamos and converted an old building on Pearl Street into a powerhouse. "I used to sleep nights on piles of pipes in the station," he recalled later, "and I saw . . . every connection made on the whole job." On September 4, 1882, the station sent its first current through the mains, and soon 5,000 lights bloomed in stores and houses all over a square-mile area. The Age of Electricity was at hand, its dawning heralded by a tiny, man-made sun, shining in a man-made glass bulb.

Edison did more than light the darkness. While giving power to the lamps of the Pearl Street district, he also gave power to its machines. Industry was quick to grasp this boon and, as a few comparative statistics show, did so with ever-mounting fervor. The initial investment in the Pearl Street venture totaled $340,000—$40,000 of it Edison's, the rest advanced by adventurous New York bankers. Today, eight decades later, the investment of electric companies in plant and equipment throughout the U.S. exceeds $50 billion. One early Edison dynamo had an output of 100 kilowatts of electric power, the equivalent of about 133 horsepower; today some generators have a potential output of 650,000 kilowatts each, the equivalent of about 870,000 horsepower. All told, in industry alone, the electric energy being used is the equivalent of 456 extra men helping every factory worker in America.

Opening a new chapter in machine history, the central power plant was, fittingly, itself a machine—a dynamo—set in motion by another machine: at Pearl Street a reciprocating steam engine, today a turbine. A highly specialized form of the wheel equipped with blades, the turbine is turned either by falling water or the expansive power of steam. The mechanical energy of the turbine (from the Latin *turbo*, "spin") drives the dynamo and sets its wire coils to spinning in the magnet's field; this generates electric energy. Transmitted to yet another machine, the electric motor, this electric energy is converted back into mechanical energy. Like the generator, the electric motor has tightly wound wire coils and a magnet. Electric current coursing through the coils initiates a push-pull interaction between magnetic fields—one created by the magnet, the other created by the electricity in the coils. This interaction makes the coils revolve at high speed. The shaft to which they are fastened revolves with them, and so, in turn, does the particular tool of the machine—the mixer or drill or grinder.

Honeymoons and horsepower

The earliest working water turbine dates back to France in the 1830s, when an organization known as the Society for the Encouragement of National Industry held a contest to improve the efficiency of the waterwheel. The winner was Benoît Fourneyron, a young engineer. In time Fourneyron designed and built turbines that delivered as much as 220 horsepower. But as prime movers they were overshadowed by the steam engine until the 1880s. Engineers then seized upon the water turbine as an ideal means of satisfying the rising demand for electric power inspired by Edison's Pearl Street station. More than a million horsepower was going to waste, for instance, in the mighty falls of Niagara; it was enough to spoil a sensible man's honeymoon. Now, however, there was a machine that could harness that wild energy. Amid coast-to-coast huzzas, Niagara's first turbogenerator, 5,000 horsepower strong, went into operation in April 1895. Soon afterward, two more were spinning away, and the power of the sublime cascade was lighting homes and driving machines in Buffalo, 22 miles away.

Today, however, hydroelectric plants produce only about 20 per cent of the nation's electric power; diesel and other internal-combustion engines furnish less than 1 per cent; a preponderant 79 per cent comes from steam-driven generators. As far back as the 1880s, Carl Gustav Patrik de Laval, a Swedish engineer, had built a small, efficient steam engine *(right)* with gracefully curved blades, somewhat like Fourneyron's water turbine. Over the next two decades, De Laval designed models which delivered 500 horsepower. In time, C. A. Parsons, a British engineer, and C. G. Curtis, an American, began building multistage turbines which were far cries from De Laval's elegant but limited machines. Sturdy

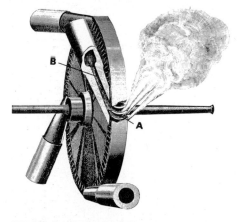

STEAM TURBINE SWEDISH-STYLE

Austere by contrast with Branca's fanciful invention *(opposite)*, workable steam turbines were built by C.G.P. de Laval, a Swedish engineer, in the 1880s. They had one wheel *(above)* which turned as fast as 40,000 rpms when steam hit its blades *(cutaway A)* and rebounded. Four nozzles provided the steam, regulating its pressure and expansion through their funnels *(cutaway B)*. Today's ram jets and rockets use the De Laval nozzle.

forerunners of the great turbines that now drive ocean liners and turn the world's biggest electric generators, these later turbines, by the early 1900s, delivered 6,500 horsepower. The modern steam turbine, some with as many as 20 wheels or more bearing some 125 blades each, delivers about 325,000 horsepower.

Of the two types of turbines, the steam-powered variety is by far the more flexible. Most hydroelectric plants need rivers of water, and, to dam them, some of the biggest, costliest works of engineering ever built by man. The steam turbine also needs water, but mostly for condensing purposes. Moreover, it can operate on a variety of fuels. Boiler heat can come from the flames of coal, gas or oil; more and more it is coming from nuclear fission. In 1963, a dozen atomic power plants with a total capacity of 900,000 kilowatts were producing electricity in the United States. Because it needs no oxygen to consume its atomic fuel, the nuclear furnace, or reactor, is particularly suited to provide steam for submarine turbines, as, for example, in the *Nautilus*.

Blessings of a distant waterfall

At one end of the kinematic chain—the chain of motion—the turbine converts natural sources of energy into electricity and sends it out over as many as 600 miles of high-voltage transmission lines; at the other end of the chain, the electric motor converts electricity into mechanical energy, into rotary motion. Thus, in effect, a distant waterfall, a blazing coal fire or a lump of disintegrating U-235 sweeps your floor and washes your dishes. No more spectacular evidence exists of the pyramiding interdependence of man and machine. A hundred years ago, if a storm blew down the poles beside a road, it mattered little. Today, by causing a power failure, a storm can disrupt the lives and work of thousands, and paralyze myriads of machines as well.

From the beginning, machine-created electric power altered ways and customs, lives and environments. One of its earliest and most influential mechanisms was the electric streetcar, which drew current from an overhead power line or third rail and relayed it to an electric motor that turned the drive wheels. Now largely displaced by swift, maneuverable gas and diesel buses, the trolley—named for a small contrivance that ran on the overhead power wire, delivering current to the car through a flexible cable—was, in its day, a formidable triumph over time and distance. It accelerated the expansion of cities by providing fast, cheap transportation between downtown and growing residential districts.

First developed in Europe, in the early 1880s, street railways soon reached America. Of the 20-odd communities using them in 1888, Richmond, Virginia, claimed to have the first line in regular service. It was built by Frank J. Sprague, then a 30-year-old Annapolis graduate, and

ELECTRICAL JOY RIDE
Retaining a hint of past modes of transport in its fringed top, the electric-powered carriage at right hurtled visitors around a small circular railway at Edison's Menlo Park, New Jersey, headquarters. Current was conveyed to the locomotive by wires attached to each rail. One passenger recalled that his ride took place "at breakneck speed [25 to 30 mph] up and down the grades, around sharp curves, over humps and bumps."

consisted of 40 cars and 12 miles of tracks. Sprague's system was an instantaneous hit; when, a few years later, New Orleans used it to replace her antiquated mule cars, jubilant citizens tossed handbills in the air reading, "Lincoln set the slaves free; Sprague set the mule free; the long-haired mule shall no longer adorn our streets."

Emulating the streetcars, the railroads turned to electricity for power in 1895. The electrification of railroad trackage by means of a third rail or overhead line for power and the changeover to locomotives driven by electric motor took time; even so, the puffing steam locomotive had the mark of doom upon it. The finish came, finally, in the 1930s and 1940s, with the successful development of the diesel electric locomotive and its three-unit power combination: oil-fueled diesel engine spinning a generator that creates electric current to drive traction motors. The last main-line steam locomotive in the U.S. was built in 1952.

These heavy electrical units ushered in modern rail transportation. But still more dramatic was the impact of small, portable electric motors. In the last 25 years—in historical perspective, a twinkling—they have reconstructed the lives of all of us, rural and urban dweller alike.

Electricity on the farm is a comparatively recent phenomenon. In 1935, although many farms utilized electric power from small, gasoline-powered generators, service from central generating stations was available to less than 11 per cent of all farms. By 1940, however, 30 per cent had such service, by 1960 no less than 97 per cent. As a result, electric motors on American farms today drive more than 100 different time- and work-saving machines, from fans to fuel pumps, from egg coolers to tool grinders, from milking machines to automatic barn cleaners.

Whether in the city or country, the small electric motor for the home, with an energy output of one fifth of a horsepower for a portable electric fan, two fifths of a horsepower for a refrigerator motor, and two thirds of a horsepower for a vacuum cleaner, has done far more to shore up the housewife than the ancient water mill accomplished for Antipater's toilworn Mediterranean maidens of the First Century B.C. In 1962, for example, the average American family consumed 4,193 kilowatt-hours of electricity, representing about nine horsepower-hours a day —the work-equivalent of 23 men laboring eight hours a day every day of the year. The cost? Perhaps $100.

A trio with a past

The three hardest-working household machines—the vacuum cleaner, dishwasher and clothes washer—are in their basic principles by no means products of our times. Indeed, they date back to the 1860s. All hinged primarily—as most do today—on the action of small, revolving fans or rotors. The early carpet cleaner had a fan rotated by means of a geared

wheel pushed across the carpet; the fan obligingly lifted the dust off the floor and blew it into a pan. The early dishwasher consisted of a tub fitted with a circular rack that held dishes at an angle, as in some modern models; a circular, bladed fan, turned manually by a crank, threw the water against and between the dishes, "impinging," in the words of the patent, "both upon their front and rear surfaces and thus washing them effectually." The 19th Century prototype of today's washing machine also consisted of a tub fitted with a rotor of several blades. A hand crank revolved the rotor in the tub and the rotor, in turn, forced a flow of cleansing water through the clothes.

Some five decades had to pass before the electric motor was small enough and efficient enough to drive a vacuum cleaner suction fan; the first upright electric model went on sale in about 1907. Electric clothes washers did not command a sizable market until the 1920s, the electric dishwasher not until the 1950s.

Whatever its separate blessings, electricity has, beyond all else, provided us with the ideal silent servant that has at last replaced our hands, our backs and our muscles. It has brought new and crackling life to the long affair between man and machine. It has bound man and machine more tightly, more closely, than ever before, forming with them a new trinity of work and achievement.

Household Machines
and
How They Work

The modern American household teems with a gleaming assortment of willing mechanical slaves. Some, such as the faucet *(opposite)*, are quite simple and have been around for a long time; others, such as the automatic toaster, have been on the scene only a few decades. Some are merely newfangled gadgets doing old-fashioned jobs (the oil burner, the refrigerator); others, such as the telephone, perform wonders never dreamed of a century ago. All are designed to make life easier. All are accepted with the nonchalance bred of a technological system which makes the miraculous seem commonplace. And yet, few who use them have the faintest idea how they work. The following pages offer a simplified guide to the functioning of six stanch household friends. Though not a repairman's manual, the guide provides an insight into what happens when a key is turned in the lock or the thermostat is turned down for the night.

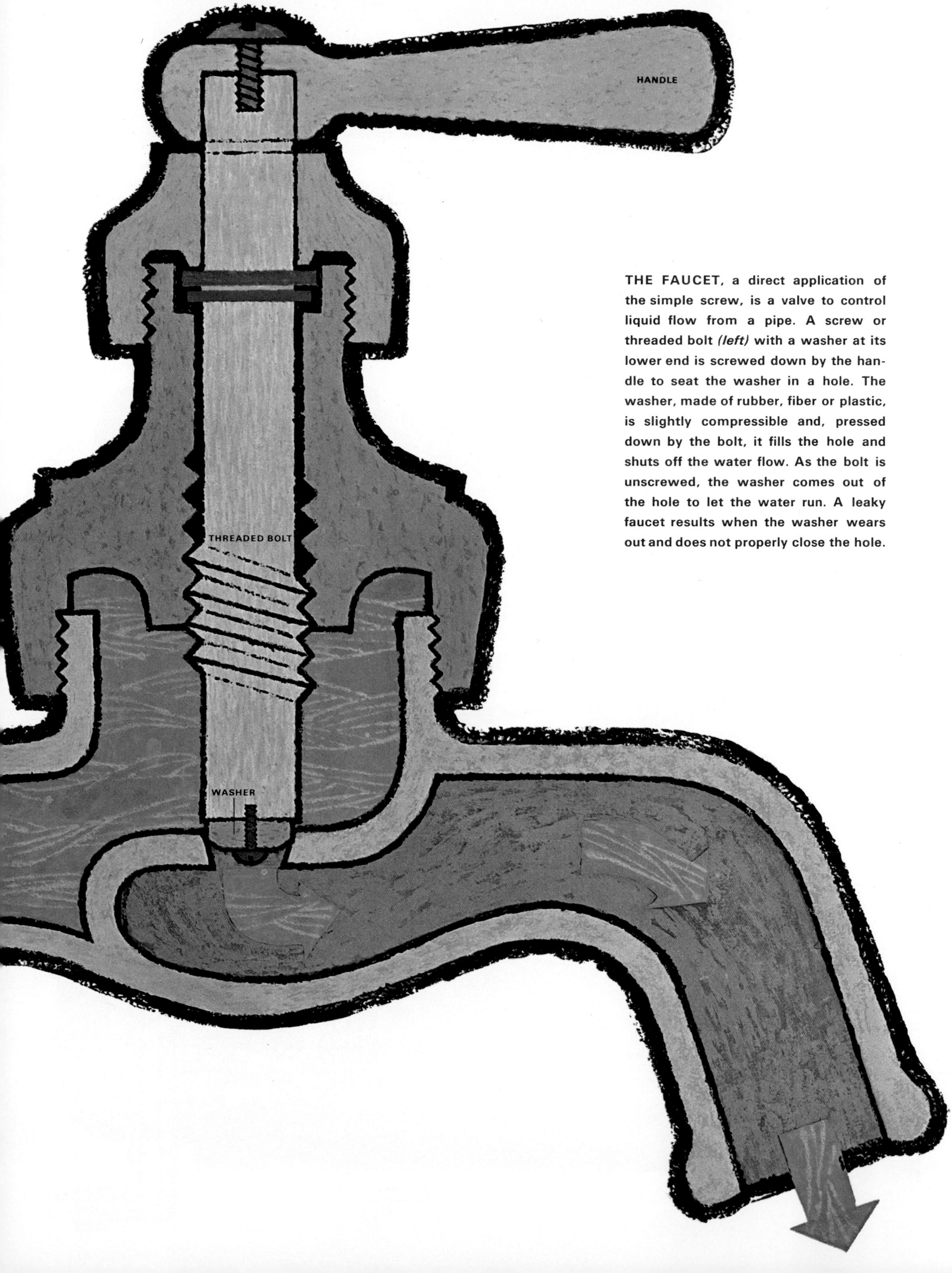

HANDLE

THREADED BOLT

WASHER

THE FAUCET, a direct application of the simple screw, is a valve to control liquid flow from a pipe. A screw or threaded bolt *(left)* with a washer at its lower end is screwed down by the handle to seat the washer in a hole. The washer, made of rubber, fiber or plastic, is slightly compressible and, pressed down by the bolt, it fills the hole and shuts off the water flow. As the bolt is unscrewed, the washer comes out of the hole to let the water run. A leaky faucet results when the washer wears out and does not properly close the hole.

The Automatic Toaster: Measured Heat from Glowing Coils

The automatic toaster may never change the course of history, but it has unquestionably won a permanent place in America's modern kitchens.

The first crude electric toaster was probably made two decades after Edison fashioned his light bulb, and it used the same principle: current put through certain kinds of wire meets resistance and heats the wire to a hot glow. (This principle is also the basis for today's electric stoves, heaters, irons and rotisseries.)

Early toasters were nonautomatic; but in 1918 a Minnesota mechanic, one Charles Strite, tired of burned toast, devised a clockwork timer to turn off the current at the right time. As the innovation caught on, Strite's clock timer gave way to a thermostat, and other refinements—such as an electric motor to lower and raise the bread—were added to attract the consumer. Now toasters account for more than four million dollars in U.S. business a year. These drawings illustrate how they work.

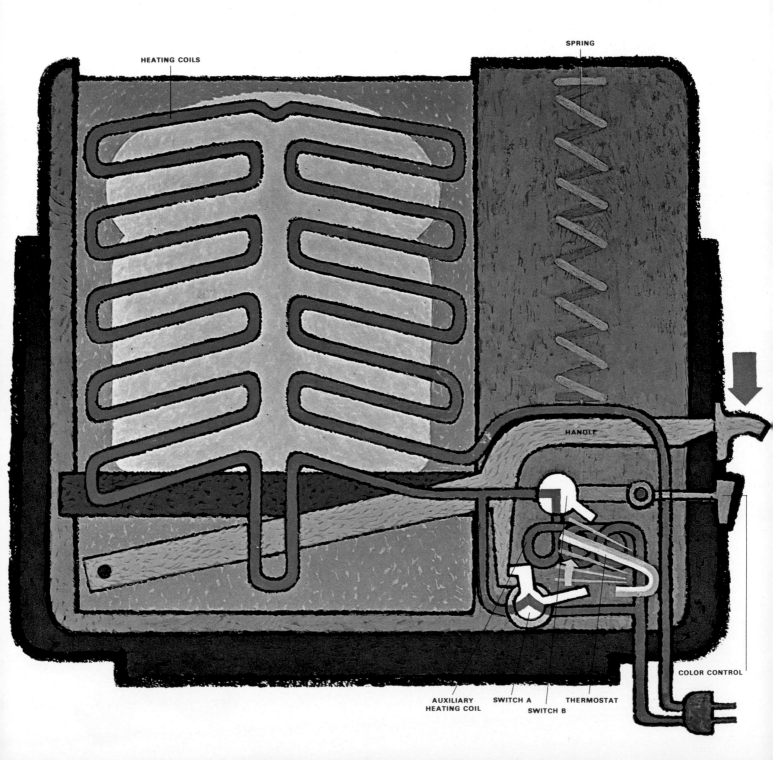

HEATING COILS

SPRING

HANDLE

AUXILIARY HEATING COIL

SWITCH A

SWITCH B

THERMOSTAT

COLOR CONTROL

TOASTING TO TASTE, an automatic toaster has to accomplish three tasks: toast the bread just the right amount, turn itself off and pop the toast up. How this happens is shown here.

It all begins when bread is placed in the slot and the handle is depressed *(opposite)*. When the handle hits bottom it is locked in place by a latch on Switch A. The handle also closes Switch A and completes a circuit, allowing electricity to flow to the toasting coils. These are made of a nickel-chromium alloy which resists the current's flow; the coils glow red-hot and cook the bread.

Depressing the handle has also closed Switch B; this completes a secondary circuit and current flows into an auxiliary heating coil, which starts warming the thermostat. The thermostat is a thin bar made of strips of two metals which expand at different rates. The coil's heat makes the bottom strip expand faster, bending the finger up till it hits Switch B and turns it off. Now, the circuit is broken, the auxiliary coil cools, and the thermostat bends back down *(below)*. When it hits Switch A it turns off the toasting coils and releases the handle, which, pulled by the spring, pops the toast up. The color-control knob determines the degree of toasting. Pushing the knob down raises Switch B, so the thermostat has to make a longer trip to turn the auxiliary coil off—thus letting the toast cook longer and get darker.

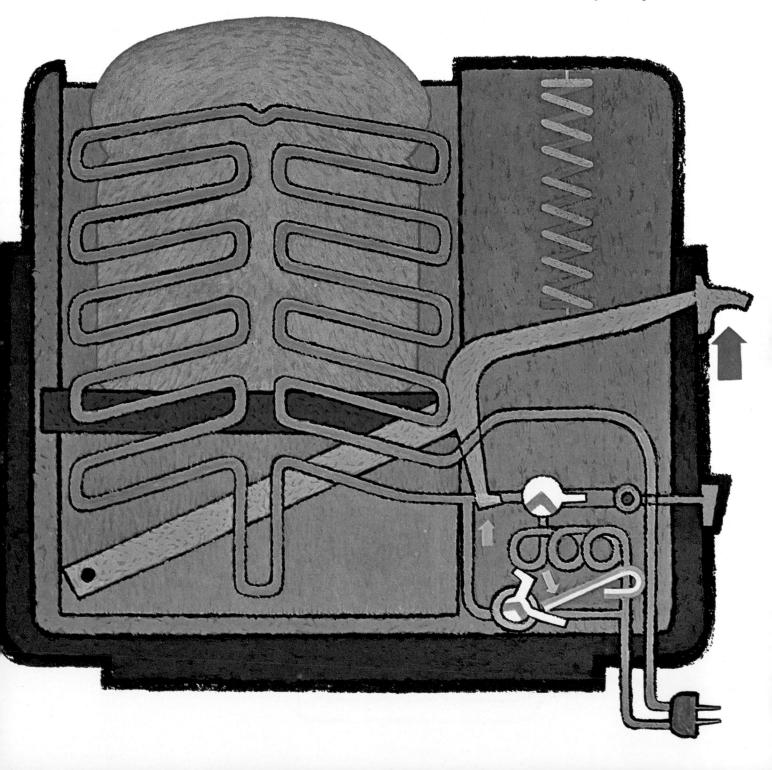

The Telephone: An Ingenious Imitator of Sound

When Alexander Graham Bell contrived his first working telephone in 1876, the world was accustomed to the clacking of the telegraph's coded messages. But, to have the actual sound of a human voice come out of a wire seemed, to a startled public, to be close to black magic.

Today the telephone is commonplace, an indispensable machine of modern living. In the U.S. alone, 82 million sets provide almost one telephone for every two people. But for most modern phone users, the way the telephone works is still a mystery. These drawings give a simplified explanation of the "magic" involved.

Sound waves do not travel far or fast. An electrical message, on the other hand, can travel through miles of wire at close to the speed of light. The whole purpose of a telephone, therefore, is to translate the sound waves of a voice into electric impulses and to convert the electricity back into sound. This is accomplished by two ingenious devices—transducers, one each in the mouthpiece and earpiece. In the mouthpiece, the transducer changes sound waves of the voice to electrical patterns. The transducer in the earpiece converts these back into sound. The sound that comes out of the receiver is so much like the voice of the caller that we seldom think of it as what it really is— merely an excellent mechanical imitation.

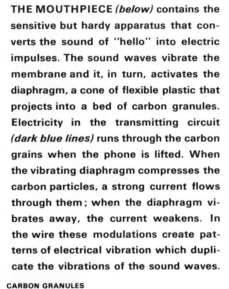

THE MOUTHPIECE *(below)* contains the sensitive but hardy apparatus that converts the sound of "hello" into electric impulses. The sound waves vibrate the membrane and it, in turn, activates the diaphragm, a cone of flexible plastic that projects into a bed of carbon granules. Electricity in the transmitting circuit *(dark blue lines)* runs through the carbon grains when the phone is lifted. When the vibrating diaphragm compresses the carbon particles, a strong current flows through them; when the diaphragm vibrates away, the current weakens. In the wire these modulations create patterns of electrical vibration which duplicate the vibrations of the sound waves.

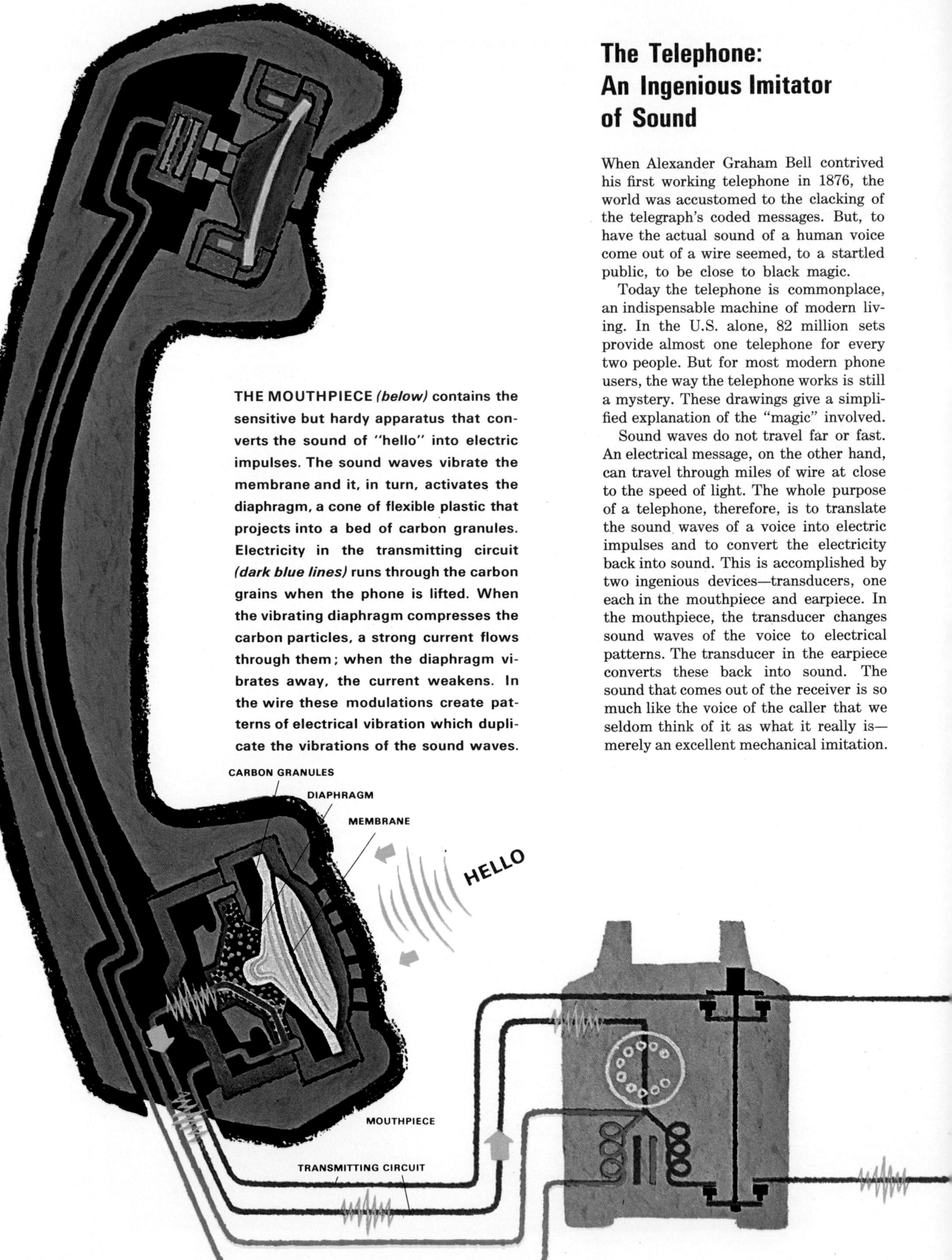

CARBON GRANULES

DIAPHRAGM

MEMBRANE

HELLO

MOUTHPIECE

TRANSMITTING CIRCUIT

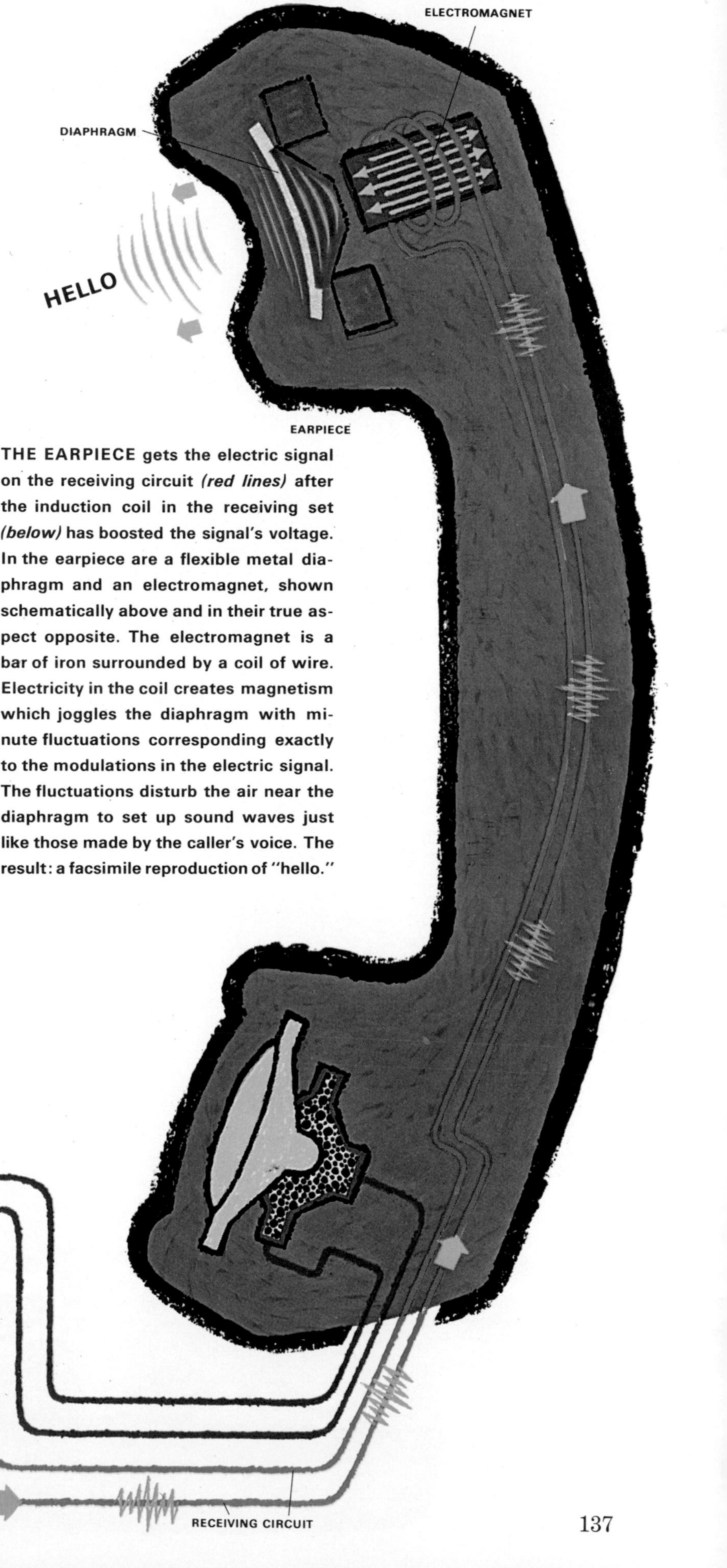

ELECTROMAGNET

DIAPHRAGM

HELLO

EARPIECE

THE SIGNAL travels through a circuit *(dark blue lines)* on its way to the receiving set. The transmitting circuit gets power from an electric generator *(below)*. The current in this circuit is much less powerful than that in a house circuit. It takes one thousandth as much power to carry a telephone message as it does to heat a toaster. The message usually is carried in wires on poles, or under ground or under water in cables. On many long-distance calls, the signal is converted into microwaves—extremely short radiowaves that are beamed across country—and then turned back into electric impulses. The signal then goes by wire to the phone being called.

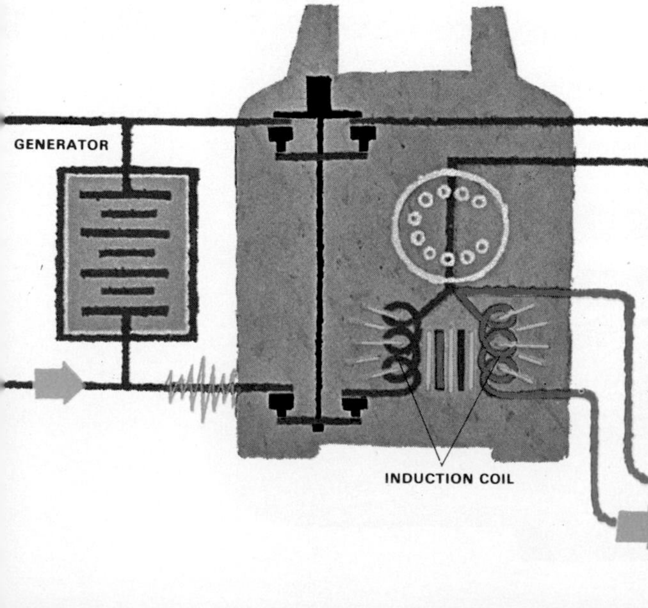

THE EARPIECE gets the electric signal on the receiving circuit *(red lines)* after the induction coil in the receiving set *(below)* has boosted the signal's voltage. In the earpiece are a flexible metal diaphragm and an electromagnet, shown schematically above and in their true aspect opposite. The electromagnet is a bar of iron surrounded by a coil of wire. Electricity in the coil creates magnetism which joggles the diaphragm with minute fluctuations corresponding exactly to the modulations in the electric signal. The fluctuations disturb the air near the diaphragm to set up sound waves just like those made by the caller's voice. The result: a facsimile reproduction of "hello."

GENERATOR

INDUCTION COIL

RECEIVING CIRCUIT

BIMETALLIC STRIP

RELAY

TEMPERATURE CONTROL   CONTACT

MOTOR

THE THERMOSTAT is activated by a curved strip that is half copper, half steel. The copper *(purple)* contracts faster, so when the room cools, the strip bends to touch the electric contact, and starts the furnace. The knob controls temperature by varying the gap between contact and strip. The relay joins the thermostat to the house current.

TRANSFORMER

FAN

HIGH-PRESSURE OIL

AIR

PRESSURE-REGULATING SCREW

LOW-PRESSURE OIL

PUMP

138

The Oil Burner: Modern Flamethrower in the Basement

Prominent citizens of ancient Rome warmed their *palazzos* with heating systems in which gases from open fires were circulated through flues in the walls. These systems were known as hypocausts. Now, 2,000 years later, we do essentially the same thing, only we call it central heating.

Today, we pipe hot water or steam, or circulate hot air through our houses; and to heat the water or air in many up-to-date systems the hypocaust's open fire is replaced by the oil burner illustrated on these pages. It uses two of man's most efficient energy sources, petroleum and electricity; and it works under the control of a simple but ingenious device which makes the whole operation automatic: the thermostat *(top left, opposite)*.

The first oil-burner patent was taken out as long ago as 1885—for a "furnace to burn oleaginous matter." But not until the late 1920s, when "oleaginous matter" for home use was generally available (as was electricity to control, pump and fire the oil) did oil burners seriously challenge the supremacy of coal fires. Since then, oil burners—more expensive than coal furnaces to operate but cleaner and far less troublesome—have moved into the basements of more than 10 million U.S. homes. The high-pressure gun-type burner shown here is by far the most widely used.

OPERATION of the burner begins when the thermostat completes a circuit to start the electric motor. The motor does two jobs: (1) it whirls a fan which blows air down the blast tube; (2) it turns a simple gear-type pump which forces fuel oil under pressure through a screw valve to the nozzle. At the same time a transformer boosts the house current's 115 volts to a jolting 10,000 volts—enough to make a spark jump between the electrodes *(below)* and ignite the oil.

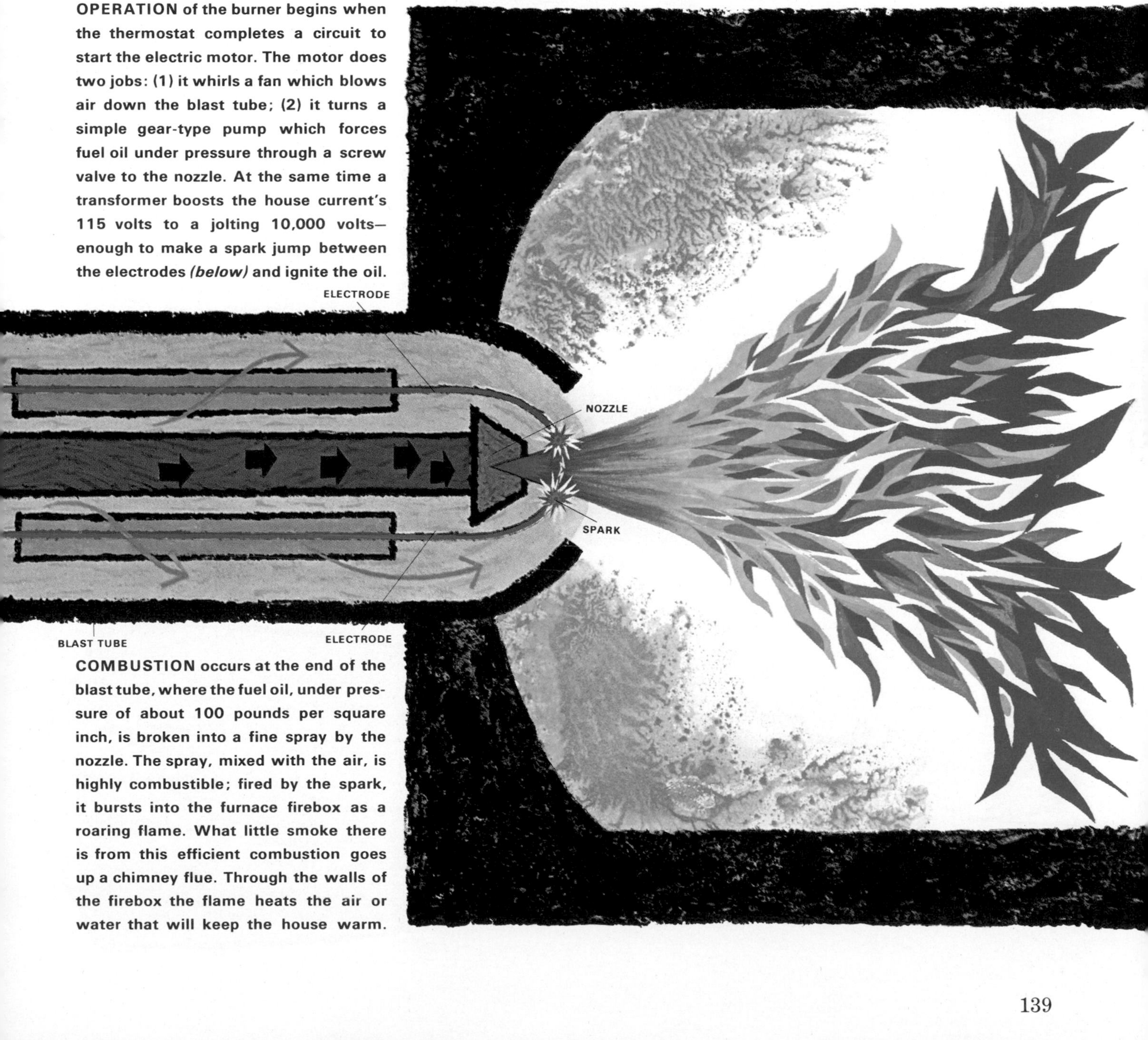

ELECTRODE

NOZZLE

SPARK

BLAST TUBE

ELECTRODE

COMBUSTION occurs at the end of the blast tube, where the fuel oil, under pressure of about 100 pounds per square inch, is broken into a fine spray by the nozzle. The spray, mixed with the air, is highly combustible; fired by the spark, it bursts into the furnace firebox as a roaring flame. What little smoke there is from this efficient combustion goes up a chimney flue. Through the walls of the firebox the flame heats the air or water that will keep the house warm.

ALMOST PICK-PROOF. The modern pin-tumbler cylinder lock is a large "shell" in which a small cylinder called the "plug" can rotate *(right)*. Five chambers drilled through both shell and plug contain springs which press down on tiny orange "drivers." These in turn press on five blue "pins." With no key in the plug's keyhole, all the pins rest on the "keyway ridge" at the base of the five chambers. The plug cannot rotate because the points at which the pins and drivers meet vary from pair to pair and do not align at the "shear point."

SHELL

SPRING

DRIVER

SHEAR POINT

PIN

TAIL

KEYWAY RIDGE

PLUG

LOCK CASE

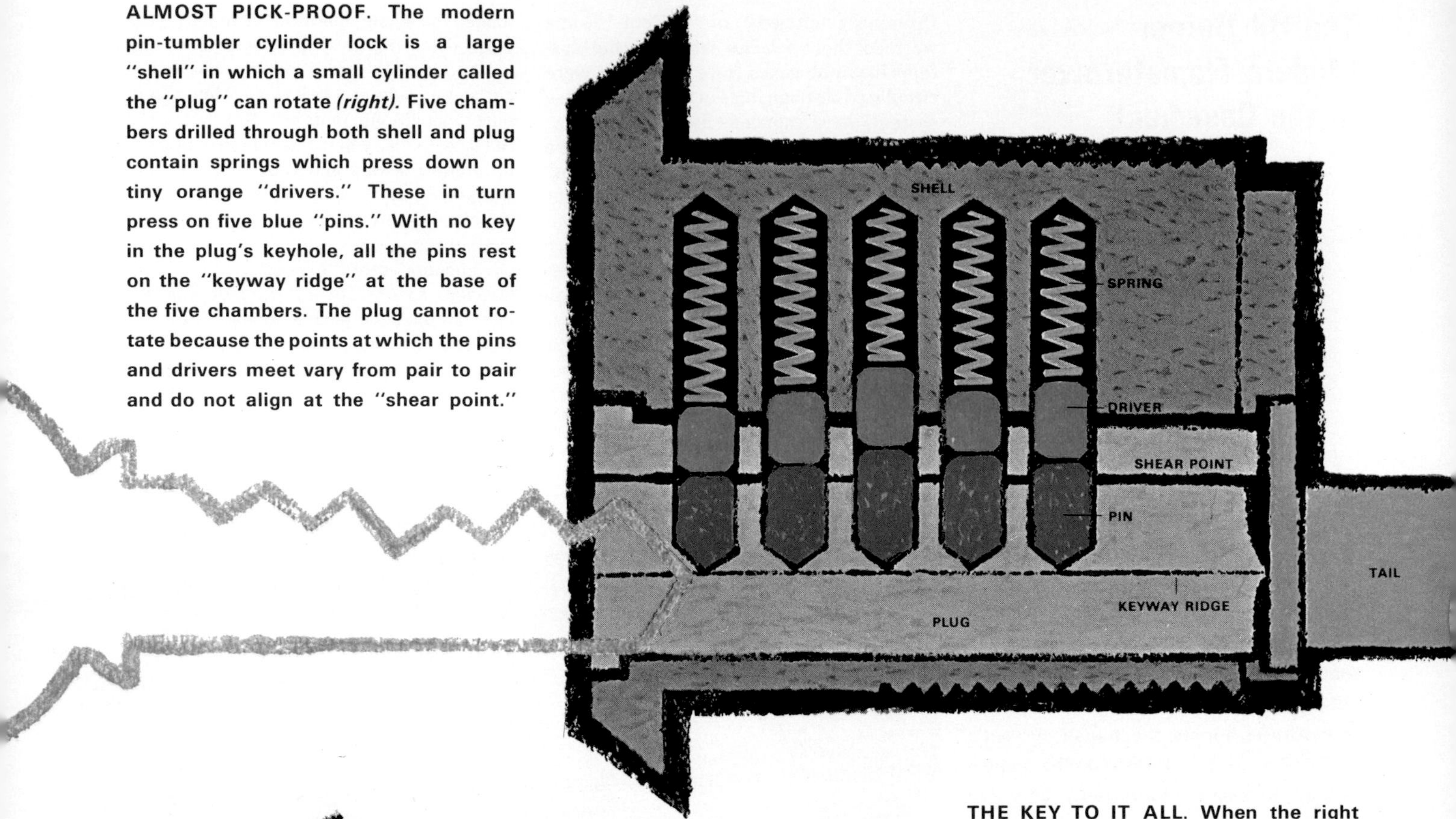

THE KEY TO IT ALL. When the right key is inserted in the plug's keyhole *(left)*, each pin settles into the key's notch directly below it. Each notch has been cut to a specific depth—for this particular lock—so that the pins align at the shear point. With all pins now entirely in the plug and all drivers entirely in the shell, the plug may be rotated by turning the key *(left, below)*. This rotates the "tail" and turns the cam *(below)*. The cam pushes the bolt's shoulder—moving the bolt in the direction of the arrows, unlocking the door.

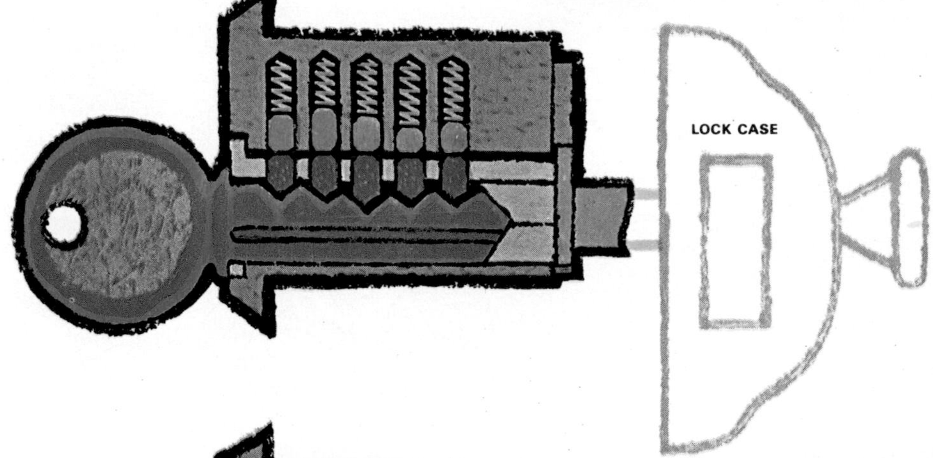

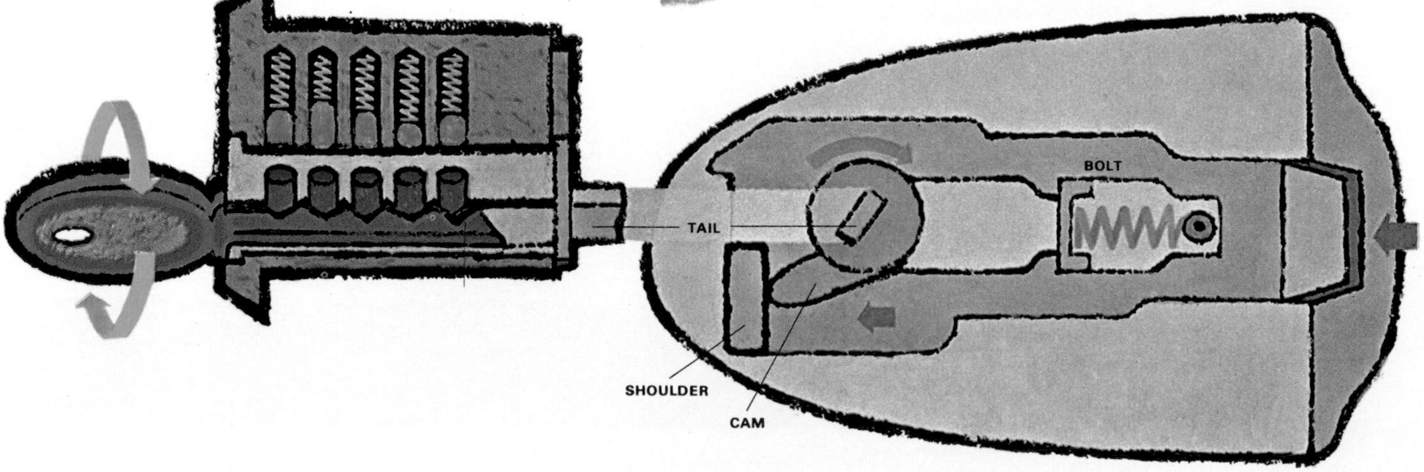

BOLT

TAIL

SHOULDER

CAM

Age-old Game of Skill: The Locksmith versus the Lockpicker

From the huge boulder the caveman rolled in front of his home to the virtually unpickable time locks of modern banks, the history of security devices is a fascinating story about people wanting to break into some place they should not.

The ancient Greeks developed an effective lock whose only drawback was the size of the key—so large it had to be carried rifle-style on the owner's shoulder. Medieval locksmiths were obsessed with building locks that offered sure-fire protection—a pistol that shot the lockpicker, a knife that amputated his fingers. The inventors of India handled the problem with more gentility: they contrived the "Hindu puzzle lock," built in the shape of a bird, the keyhole hidden in the wing.

Locking up the modern world began in earnest in 18th Century England with the invention of a lever-tumbler lock *(right)*. Yet, in spite of British ingenuity, the lock center of the world—for making *and* picking—moved across the ocean. In 1851 the American locksmith Alfred Hobbs boasted he could pick the best locks the English showed him but that no Englishman could pick his. He was proved right on both counts. Finally, in the 1860s, an obscure American portrait painter, following in his father's footsteps, turned to lockmaking and perfected the ingenious modern pin-tumbler lock *(opposite)*, thus making his surname known in every American home. Even today, however, few Americans know his full name: Linus Yale Jr.

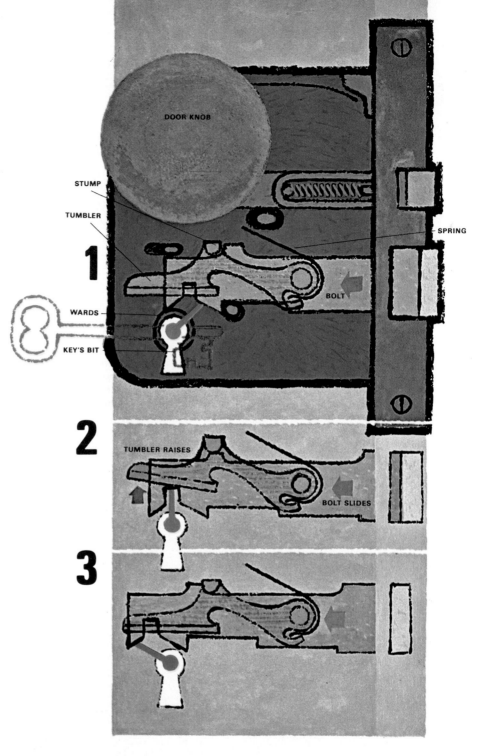

1 The heart of the old-fashioned lever-tumbler lock is the "tumbler" *(blue, above)*. Held in place behind the bolt *(olive)* by a spring, the tumbler is simply a lever with a projection called the "stump." Since the stump blocks a similar projection on the bolt, it keeps the bolt from moving in the direction of the arrow. The key's "bit" is beginning its twofold job: its front will lift the tumbler; its back will slip into the notch of the bolt, moving the bolt to the left.

2 The bit has been turned through 180°. Its front half has already lifted the tumbler high enough *(vertical arrow)* so that the stump no longer impedes the bolt's movement *(horizontal arrow)*. Simultaneously, the back of the bit has engaged the bolt and started unlocking the door. A key's bit is slotted to enable it to avoid a pattern of raised obstacles called "wards," in the rear wall of the lock it was made to open. A key with a different slot pattern will not fit the lock.

3 The key has pulled the bolt as far to the left as it will go; the bit has already passed out of the bolt's notch; the door is unlocked. To lock it, all the operations should be read in reverse. Lever-tumbler locks are easy to pick—which is why, for maximum security, they have been gradually replaced by cylinder locks *(opposite)* over the last 100 years. All that is needed is a simple "skeleton key" whose bit is thin enough to bypass all the wards inside the lock.

The Refrigerator: Keeping Things Cold by Coming to a Boil

Of all the shiny new appliances serving in today's kitchens, perhaps the most puzzling in its operation is the refrigerator. Quiet, and automatic, it starts getting cold when it is plugged into an electric outlet, an action that usually generates heat (lighted lamps, stoves, steam irons, toasters). These diagrams give an idea of the process which keeps the ice cream hard and the butter fresh.

The first workable refrigerating machine was built in 1834 by Jacob Perkins, an American engineer. His clumsy device, used in such commercial operations as ice plants, meat-packing houses and breweries, was a far cry from today's sleek machines; but the basic ingredient was the same: a singular substance called a refrigerant which boils and condenses (changes from liquid to vapor and vice versa) at freezing temperatures. Early machines used sulphur dioxide as a refrigerant, but now most home refrigerators use Freon, a refrigerant designed especially for the job.

The refrigerator's secret is to let cold liquid Freon absorb heat coming from the food inside. The heat boils the Freon and turns it into a vapor—which can be made to give up the heat while being reliquefied. As a liquid, the Freon is sent back to the freezer, ready to pick up more heat.

ABSORBING HEAT from food in the refrigerator, liquid Freon boils in the freezer at arctic temperatures, and becomes a vapor *(yellow)*. This goes to the compressor, where, as described below, it is put under high pressure and heated to above room temperature. In the condenser, which has cooling fins as in a car's radiator, the vapor releases some of its heat to the room. At about room temperature, the vapor condenses, becoming a liquid again *(blue)*. This occurs, although the Freon is far above its normal liquefying temperature, because it is under pressure.

Freon moves up to a valve which restricts flow and thus maintains the pressure behind it. As the Freon comes through the valve, pressure drops; now, since it is well above its boiling point for the new pressure, some of the Freon immediately vaporizes. Energy in the form of heat is required to turn a liquid into a vapor, and the Freon uses its own heat as it boils, thus reducing its temperature to below freezing. Warm air rises *(arrows)* to be absorbed—and make the rest of the Freon boil—while the cold air moves down through the refrigerator. The refrigeration cycle operates only when the rising inside temperature activates a thermostat, which closes a switch to start the compressor motor.

MIDWAY THROUGH INTAKE PHASE

CYLINDER
RING
LOW-PRESSURE VAPOR
INTAKE PORT: FROM FREEZER
BARRIER
OUTLET PORT: TO CONDENSER
CAM
HIGH-PRESSURE VAPOR

MIDWAY THROUGH THE CYCLE

MIDWAY THROUGH OUTLET PHASE

THE OBJECT of the rotary compressor is to draw Freon vapor down from the freezer and pump it out under pressure into the condenser. It is made up of a cylinder, a steel ring attached to a cam, and a spring-loaded barrier which separates the exit and intake ports.

THE ROTATION of the cam by an electric motor rolls the off-centered ring around against the cylinder wall, leaving a crescent-shaped space which is filled with vapor. The barrier slides in and out of its housing, always pressing against the ring with a vapor-tight seal.

THE RESULT of the ring's rotation is shown in these diagrams. Compression occurs because of a valve in the system *(opposite)* which backs up the Freon as the ring pushes the vapor ahead of it out into the condenser. The compression also makes the vapor heat up.

7

Master Keys to
an Age of
Communication

THE COMPULSION TO COMMUNICATE RUNS DEEP. Long before the discovery of electricity, men found ways to transmit information faster than they could walk, run or ride. They sent it in puffs of smoke, in the sound of tom-toms, horns, bells or pistol shot, in the flash of metal or mirror in the sun, the gleam of belfry lanterns by night.

Today our lines of communication reach across continents and oceans. For this miracle, responsibility rests with a new breed of machine—mechanisms that utilize electricity's invisible waves, flows and forces. These electric machines range from crude devices activated by currents pulsing through their thin metallic nerves to masterly devices which have come to be called "electronic" because they depend on the action of electrons in vacuum tubes and transistors. These mechanisms extend our senses even as earlier machines extended our muscles. They have also extended the very meaning of the word "machine." Now it includes not only a mass of shining, spinning wheels and gears, but also a little black box, crammed with instruments and wires, sitting in a corner or on a shelf.

Electronic machines bring into our living rooms the President of the United States or a skirmish in a thatched village on the Congo. With squiggling pens and leaping oscillograph lines they record our heartbeats, the activity of our brains, the movement of our eyes in dreaming slumber. They provide Proustian keys to the past, enabling us to hear again voices long stilled. Primary among these extraordinary machines of communication and memory are the telegraph, telephone and radio; the phonograph and magnetic tape recorder; the sound motion picture; and the stupendous synthesis of something from all of them—television.

Inseparable though they may seem from the 20th Century, electronic machines have their roots deep in the past, in the gradual accrual of knowledge about the conduction and insulation of electric current. In 1729, an Englishman, Stephen Gray, transmitted electric charges nearly 300 yards over lines of moistened thread and brass wire. Two decades later, a Frenchman, the Abbé Jean Antoine Nollet, decided to find out how fast electricity traveled. A man of humor as well as scientific curiosity, he arranged 200 Carthusian monks in a mile-round circle, wired them together, sent a stiff charge through the wire—and learned that it traveled very fast indeed. But essentially it was the work of Volta, Oersted and Henry, described in Chapter 6, that launched electronics on its way—Volta's battery, Oersted's discovery of electromagnetism, and Henry's electromagnet.

The electromagnet is, in fact, crucial to all communications machines. The typical electromagnet—such as the one in a telephone receiver—is a small iron core wrapped in coils of insulated wire. As noted earlier, it is activated by the magnetizing properties of electric current. When cur-

ENCORES WITHOUT END
Along with the urge to share his words and thoughts, man has always had the desire to give them permanence. Edison's talking machine *(opposite)* effected a happy fusion of these goals. His 1908 Model D brought the expressions of talented strangers into the American home. Imprinted on wax, their words and songs could be enjoyed over and over again.

rent courses through the coils, the core becomes magnetic. It is incredibly responsive; whether the current vibrates on and off 50 or 50,000 times a second, so many times does the core gain and lose its magnetism, precisely reflecting and radiating the current's strength and duration.

In England in the 1830s, W. F. Cooke, a medical student, and Charles Wheatstone, a physicist, drew on Oersted's discovery that a magnetic needle is deflected by electric current, and devised a primitive electric telegraph (*shown on page 148*) that dramatically foreshadowed modern police teletype communication. On New Year's Day, 1845, one John Tawell fatally poisoned a woman of Slough, then fled aboard a train for London, 18 miles away. Authorities telegraphed Tawell's description ahead. London detectives were awaiting him when he arrived at Paddington Station. In due course he was hanged for murder.

Brainstorm of a portrait painter

Concurrently with the Cooke-Wheatstone effort, Samuel F. B. Morse, an American portrait painter, decided to invent an electric telegraph of his own. A brilliantly simple device, it established the basic principle of all electromagnetic communications machines to follow: conversion of information into electric pulses—brief, intermittent beats—and its transmission as electric signals. Telephone, radio, television and magnetic tape all do this. So, fascinatingly enough, do our senses; they pick up information about our environment, convert it into nerve signals and flash them to the brain.

The Morse telegraph consisted of a source of electric power—at first a battery, later voltage from a central station—a sending key, a receiver in the form of an electromagnetic sounder, and a connecting wire. Pressure on the key activated the sounder's electromagnet. The magnet then moved the sounder with an audible click. As a complement to his apparatus, Morse devised his now celebrated code of "dots" and "dashes." Each letter and number had its own identity; the letter "a," for instance, was "dot-dash." The merest touch of the key would send a "dot." If held down a fraction of a second longer, it would send a "dash."

After a prolonged Congressional ruckus over the absurdity of Morse's contraption, the government awarded him $30,000 to construct a 38-mile telegraph line between Baltimore and Washington. Using small glass plates for insulators, he strung his wire from poles along the B & O right of way. The first message went over the wire May 1, 1844. Learning that the Whigs in national convention in Baltimore had just named Henry Clay and Theodore Frelinghuysen as their candidates for President and Vice President, Alfred Vail, Morse's assistant, sat down at his key at nearby Annapolis Junction and tapped out, "The ticket is Clay and Frelinghuysen." These words—history's first news flash—beat

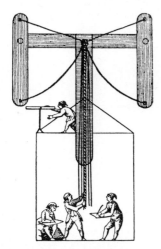

ELOQUENCE IN WOOD

One of the most successful precursors of the electric telegraph was invented in the 1790s by a young French revolutionary, Claude Chappe. It consisted of a wooden crossbeam with movable arms, or semaphores, for transmitting messages received by an observer armed with telescope from another Chappe station a few miles away. The arms could be adjusted in 192 different positions, representing letters, words and even whole phrases.

the returning delegates' train to Washington by an hour and four minutes. On May 24, at formal ceremonies in the chamber of the Supreme Court, Morse dispatched to Baltimore the first official message of his telegraph, appropriately a passage from Numbers, 23: 23: "What hath God wrought!" The pulses he tapped out covered the distance between the two cities in a little less than 1/4,900 of a second.

In two years, telegraph wires webbed north from Washington to Portland, Maine, west to Milwaukee. They were by no means universally regarded as a boon. In one area farmers tore down miles of wire in the conviction that it drew electricity from the air, upset the weather and ruined the crops. Nevertheless, the inevitable push to extend the line all the way to the Pacific could not be deterred. By 1861 the job was finished, and the valiant riders of the Pony Express went pounding over the ridge into history. Five years later the S.S. *Great Eastern* succeeded in laying Cyrus H. Field's permanent transatlantic cable from Ireland to Trinity Bay in Newfoundland. The Atlantic seaboard went wild. News that yesterday took 12 days by steamer could now be relayed by Morse code between New York and London in minutes. Never again would the world seem so big.

Morse's device, tirelessly clicking its code signals in railroad stations and telegraph offices, soon led imaginative men to believe that if such sounds could be sent over a wire, the human voice might be sent the same way. The dreamer destined to realize this feat was a dark-haired, Byronic young Scotsman living in Boston, Alexander Graham Bell. A speech professor and teacher of lip reading, Bell decided to apply his knowledge of acoustics and the human auditory system to development of a mechanism which would convert the sound waves of the human voice into a fluctuating electric current and back again. The result was, of course, the telephone.

A spill and a sprint

At his laboratory one June day in 1875, Bell sat with a receiving apparatus pressed to his ear. In another room, an assistant, Thomas A. Watson, adjusted a steel reed attached to their experimental transmitter. Watson gave the reed a tap. Its vibrations came over the wire to Bell in a faint but unmistakable twang. The next winter, in Bell's lodgings, he and Watson set up an improved transmitter and started tests. On March 10, 1876, Bell was in his study, Watson in an adjoining bedroom. While making preliminary adjustments, Bell tipped over a bottle of acid. It spilled on his clothes. "Mr. Watson!" he cried. "Come here; I want you." Watson heard the words clearly—the first sentence spoken over a telephone. He came running. Later that same year, Bell, then just 29, received from the U.S. Patent Office Patent No. 174,465—as it

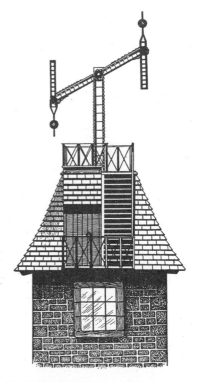

A SECRET FRENCH WEAPON

By their speed in passing along military information, Chappe semaphore stations like the one above helped France turn back the foreign armies her neighbors sent to stamp out the flames of the French Revolution. Built on hilltops, each station brandished an improved version of the wooden signal system opposite. Chappe's first "telegraph line," completed in 1794, consisted of 15 such towers spanning the 144 miles from Paris to Lille.

turned out, one of the most valuable single patents ever issued. Today's refined and mass-produced version of Bell's first successful telephone is a well-nigh indispensable instrument; by 1962, some 150 million were in use the world over.

Even as Bell put his invention into commercial service in 1878, another dream began to tug at man. He now had proof that through the exciting agency of electricity, the human voice as well as Morse's dot-and-dash code could be effectively sent over a wire. But why—he began to ask himself—a wire? Wires were costly to erect; storms blew them down. Could electricity, the miracle worker, make possible a machine for sending messages through the air *without* wire?

In 1894, after months of experiments, an inspired Italian youth of only 20, Guglielmo Marconi, invited his mother to his attic laboratory in their home near Bologna. As she looked on, he pressed a button. Though there were no connecting wires, a bell rang in the living room two stories below: wireless transmission was an accomplished fact. From his father, somewhat reluctant because he considered his son an impractical dreamer, Marconi borrowed 5,000 lire—then about $1,000—to develop his invention further. Three years later, in England, he sent wireless code signals over distances up to eight miles. From then on, it was merely a question of building more powerful transmitters, more sensitive receivers, of refinements in instrumentation and technology. After two more years, Marconi was able to flash a wireless message across the English Channel, and soon ironclads of the British fleet, under simulated battle conditions, communicated with each other at distances of 60 miles.

Conquest in three clicks

Next Marconi traveled across the Atlantic. In a small, experimental wireless station on Signal Hill, St. John's, Newfoundland, on December 12, 1901, he pressed to his ear a telephone receiver connected to his delicately adjusted receiving apparatus. Above the station, 400 feet up, a large kite roved the bleak, blustery sky at the end of a slender copper-wire antenna. At precisely 12:30 p.m. Newfoundland time, Marconi heard what he had strained and hoped to hear—a prearranged signal from his powerful transmitter at Cornwall, England. Three brief clicks came in through the crash and squeal of static, three dots—Morse code for the letter "s." In 1/86 of a second, a call from one man to another had spanned 2,170 miles of ocean.

The concept behind this epic moment had not, obviously, come to Marconi as a bolt from the blue. But it was his genius to assemble and improve upon the ideas and devices of other men, notably two physicists who had studied the dynamics of electromagnetic waves—the vibrating, invisible sea that is all around us, that now faithfully distributes, be-

MESSAGES BY MAGNET

The Cooke-Wheatstone telegraph of the 1830s, one of the first to operate by electromagnetism, had five needles placed midway across a lattice. Pressure on two keys activated magnets to tilt the needles in the direction of different letters of the alphabet. The needles' pattern was then transmitted by wire to the receiving station, where the needles of an identical machine were deflected in the same way, providing the "coded" message.

yond the horizon of man, the teeming signals of radio and television.

The first of these physicists was James Clerk Maxwell of Cambridge University. Maxwell figured out the basic mathematical equations of electromagnetism, and in 1865 used them to postulate the existence of electromagnetic waves that traveled through space with the 186,000-miles-per-second speed of light, radiating from their source as ripples in a pond radiate from the impact point of a tossed stone. The second physicist, Heinrich Hertz of Germany, confirmed Maxwell's hypothesis in the late 1880s by means of two instruments, an oscillator, or transmitter, and a detector, or receiver. Hertz was able to send electromagnetic waves through the air with the oscillator, and intercept them with the detector, though the instruments were in no way connected. These waves, known for many years as hertzian waves, are what we now call radio waves.

The many ways of a wave

Gradually their salient characteristics were unfolded. Their rate of oscillation, or frequency, was fantastic, ranging from 500,000 cycles to up to two million cycles a second. Some could follow the curvature of the earth. They all could penetrate and pass through many substances. When concentrated and beamed in very high frequencies, even through fog and darkness, they would reflect back, like an echo of light, to receivers near the transmitter—the clue, later, to radar.

Marconi's radiotelegraph produced discernible code signals in the following manner. Pressure on the key closed an electric circuit. This made a spark jump an air gap between two metal balls perhaps 1/25 of an inch apart. The spark gave off radio waves which went through the antenna and out over the air in discontinuous dot-dash bursts which the person at the receiving end could hear and decipher. Today's transmitters push out, not discontinuous bursts, but a steady flow of radio waves. By pressing a sending key, the operator can modify, or "modulate," the shape of the waves. These modulations are what the receiver translates back into sounds.

Within relatively few years after Marconi's radiotelegraph, the air was a chaos of time signals, weather reports, flashes from ships at sea and the chitchat of ham operators. The receiver was able to "tune in" the transmitter he wanted to hear because of an instrument called a variable capacitor, which screened out signals on other frequencies. The process was akin to looking at a spectrum through a slit, permitting the viewer to see one color at a time.

Basic techniques of radio remain much the same today as in Marconi's time, although, of course, with major improvements and refinements. One was the advance from radiotelegraph to radiotelephony by adapting

TRIUMPH IN TINFOIL
The world's first phonograph recording was the opening verse of "Mary Had a Little Lamb," spoken by Thomas Edison into his new talking machine. Photographed in 1878 *(below)*, the device worked when sound waves caused a needle to vibrate and impress a pattern of these vibrations on a tinfoil-covered cylinder. It caused such a sensation that President Rutherford B. Hayes invited Edison to the White House and tinkered with the machine until almost dawn.

the telephone transmitter to radio transmission; radio waves, instead of being modulated by means of telegraph keys, were modulated by means of electric signals created by sounds directed into a microphone. A second and incalculably important advance was the development of the vacuum tube, a highly sensitive electronic mechanism which could detect radio signals more efficiently than the early-day crystal detectors, and amplify them in both transmission and reception so that they could be sent farther and reproduced more loudly and clearly.

The vacuum tube was invented in 1904 by an Englishman, John Ambrose Fleming, as a result of observations that Edison made concerning his early incandescent lamps but, ironically, never pursued. Fleming's tube took radio waves as they came from the antenna and changed them from oscillations to a steady, one-way flow of current. In 1907 Dr. Lee De Forest, an American engineer, produced an improved tube called the triode, or audion. An improved circuit design, added in 1914 by E. H. Armstrong, then a Columbia University postgraduate in electrical engineering, vastly increased the audion's sensitivity and its power to amplify weak signals.

Because of its ability to magnify the feeblest electric signals with great fidelity, the vacuum tube proved the key to all the wonders of modern electronics, from radar to electron microscope, from television to computers. It added a new dimension to many machines and became, literally as well as figuratively, their small, warm, glowing, electronic heart.

The transition from mechanical machine to electronic machine was nowhere more strikingly evident than in the evolution of both the phonograph and sound motion picture. As first conceived, the phonograph—the "talking machine"—was a mechanical device for reproducing sound waves. An artist sang or played into a horn. The vibrations caused a steel needle to tremble, and to impress their pattern upon a spinning wax cylinder (later on a disc). When a home phonograph played a duplicate disc, *its* needle reproduced the original vibrations against a membrane or diaphragm that converted them back into sound waves.

From crudity to Chippendale

In 1877 an obscure French poet, Charles Cros, thought of such a talking machine, but while he was trying to raise money to develop it, Edison hit upon the same idea as he tinkered with a high-speed telegraph transmitter. A few months later, he handed one of his mechanics a rough sketch of a device. "Here," he said, "see how fast you can turn this out." Legend has it that the mechanic was back with a simple model after only 30 hours, and received $18 for his labor. From this device, with its crude, hand-cranked cylinder, Edison's talking machine ultimately progressed to windup, spring-motored models in Chinese Chippendale cabinets,

MUSIC IN THE STREETS

The music of an orchestra playing in a closed room of a pre-18th Century European theater *(above)* was transmitted to the streets by a huge acoustic horn *(cutaway above, detail at right).* Such horns were designed to capture and amplify sound waves and funnel them in one direction. The success of the phonograph in its fledgling days depended on scooping up sound with smaller acoustic horns *(opposite).*

proliferating in parlors across the land and creating a new public awareness of musical artistry.

But by the mid-1920s, Americans were beginning to listen to radio—radios which incorporated World War I improvements in microphones and vacuum-tube amplifiers. Compared to the sounds from their radios, the sounds from their phonographs were muffled, high-pitched and tinny. By 1924, Bell Telephone Laboratories researchers had successfully developed a new electrical recording technique based on vacuum-tube amplification. Like the radiotelephone, it transformed sound waves into electric signals and then brought them up, amplifying them for the master record from which thousands of duplicate pressings would be made. The range was enriched; the volume was stronger. The old mechanical talking machine was banished to the attic, dethroned by the electrical phonograph.

A parallel development occurred with another device for transforming sound into electric signals and back again—the magnetic tape recorder. As this electronic machine works today, sound waves enter the microphone; the microphone translates them into electric signals which, amplified by a vacuum tube, travel to a tiny electromagnet called the "electromagnetic head." Here they set up a flow of magnetic patterns reflecting the original sound waves. At the same time, rotating reels draw magnetic tape past the head at constant speed. One side of the tape carries plastic backing as shiny as gift-wrap ribbon; the other side is coated with myriads of iron-oxide particles held in a resinous material. These particles themselves are magnetized; as they pass through the pattern of the recording head, they instantly arrange themselves and freeze in a precise reflection of this pattern. When the tape is played back, the process is reversed. The pattern of magnetized iron particles flows past the head, which converts the pattern back into electric signals. These, amplified, come out the speaker as the original sound.

Memories made to order

A magnetic tape recorder is, in a very literal sense, a memory. It stores things—a Beethoven concerto, the sound of San Francisco foghorns, a statesman's speech, the cooings of infants. It also stores data for machines—in magnetic patterns arranged in machine language—so that, as we shall see in Chapter 8, when it is played back to a machine, it can communicate with that machine. Thus it is a machine talking with, or giving orders to, another machine. And since it permits a machine—a computer, say—to store information for later use, it can be a machine's memory too.

Electronics has enabled us to graft onto machines still another human attribute—an eye, far more sensitive and durable than the human eye,

MUSIC IN THE GROOVE
Early recording studios came into their own in the 1890s, when disc-shaped, grooved records—still familiar today—gradually replaced Edison's cylinders. In the scene above, an Edison phonograph is recording an unknown pianist. The practice became socially acceptable—and financially profitable—for artists and entertainers after the great Caruso took it up, reaping $4,000 for his first recording session alone.

yet made with a few cents' worth of wire, chemicals and glass. This is the photoelectric tube, the "electric eye"—the gadget that whips open supermarket doors, operates drinking fountains and burglar alarms, and makes possible wire or radio transmission of pictures. It also makes possible television, which, according to surveys, the average American family now spends more time in watching than in any other single activity except sleeping.

In a vacuum tube, a wire emits, or "boils off," electrons—a stream of electricity—when it is heated by electric current. In a photoelectric tube, a piece of metal emits electrons when light shines on it—a phenomenon called the "photoelectric effect." Just as the microphone converts sound waves into electric signals, so the photoelectric tube converts light waves into electric signals. These need amplifying before they acquire enough strength to trip a switch, open a door, or start or stop a motor. They can be transmitted over a wire or through the air. At their destination, machines convert them into replicas, or images, of the original light waves.

Before producing television, however, the team of photoelectric tube and vacuum tube revolutionized the motion picture. The silent movie was altogether fascinating to watch, but mute—pantomimic, two-dimensional, mechanical. To this diverting dumb show the electronic team now added words and music, the warmth of the human voice and violins, the sound as well as the sight of news.

The sounds of synthesis

The motion picture and the phototube made a strange match, marking the culmination of years of research by Lee De Forest, inventor of the audion, by George Eastman, the film maker, by General Electric researchers and many others. The resulting device—sound film—was an ingenious synthesis. The sounds, as they were recorded, were converted into electric signals, which varied the pattern of a light beam on a strip of film beside the picture frames. Converting this pattern back into sound was a simple matter of putting a photoelectric tube to work. A sharp pinpoint of light was focused against this sound track; its beam passed through the track and struck a photoelectric tube on the other side. As the film (and the track) moved between them, the varying light waves were picked up by the photoelectric tube and transformed into tiny electric signals. Vacuum tubes amplified them; loudspeakers turned them back into sound.

The photoelectric tube proved the key to other electronic processes. One was telephoto, the transmission of copies of pictures and manuscript, in minutes, by wire or radio—first achieved at the Republican National Convention in Cleveland in 1924. In a typical procedure, the sender clamps the picture to a horizontal cylinder that revolves 100

THE GLOWING HEART OF RADIO

The genie that made the modern radio possible is a small glass container with bits of metal and wire inside of it—a vacuum tube *(below)*. Inside this airless tube, excess electrons on a negatively charged filament called a "cathode" are drawn toward a positively charged plate called an "anode." Between cathode and anode is a negatively charged "grid," which carries the feeble alternating current from an antenna activated by radio waves. As this current alternates, the grid may act very negatively *(below, right)*, repelling the electrons, or it may act more positively *(below, left)*, helping pull electrons to the anode. It is the passage of electrons to the anode that amplifies the radio waves to produce sound.

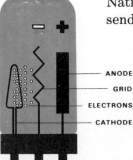

ANODE

GRID

ELECTRONS

CATHODE

152

times a minute and at the same time moves sideways. As it revolves, a thin, steady beam of light strikes the picture in a point 1/200 of an inch square, and precisely reflects the varying shades of black, white and gray in the picture. These reflections are focused into a mirror, which plays them into a photoelectric tube. The tube converts them into electric signals; vacuum tubes amplify them to transmission strength. At the receiving end, amplifiers restore power that has dwindled in passage. An electronic "light valve" transforms the signals back into varying intensities of light. These register on light-sensitive photographic film mounted on a revolving cylinder that moves as the transmitting cylinder moved. When the process is finished, the receiver has a film negative that he can use to make a positive copy of the original photograph.

The logical synthesis of all this was television: the simultaneous transmission, without wire, of sight and sound, giving us the gift of total spectatorship, as if we were, in truth, where the camera and microphone are. There was a further synthesis with magnetic tape—videotape, finally accomplished in the mid-1950s. On this could be recorded not only what the microphone heard, but also what the television camera saw, so that the moment or event could be preserved for later showing.

Dreamed of in the infant years of radio, the scanning system essential to television was finally assembled and refined in American research laboratories. Among the dozens of dedicated contributors of ideas, the names of two stand out: Vladimir K. Zworykin and Philo T. Farnsworth. Zworykin, a Russian émigré, came to America after World War I, and in 1929 demonstrated his iconoscope—the first seeing electronic eye of television. Farnsworth developed the image orthicon, today's improved television camera eye.

A case of black, white and gray

The process of televising a picture begins when the television camera lens directs the image of the subject into an image orthicon—an electron tube about 15 inches long. Inside the tube is a screen made of light-sensitive material. Upon it falls the projected image in perfect miniature. The image is composed of light waves of varying strengths; these are what make for whites, blacks and grays in a black-and-white picture. The light waves, according to their intensity, cause varying numbers of electrons to be emitted both from this screen and an adjacent target screen. An electrical image is formed on the target screen in the places left by the missing electrons.

At the opposite end of the electron tube is an electron gun—so called because when heated it shoots out a sharp, searchlight beam of electrons. This beam scans the target screen at the rate of 30 times a second, and bounces off onto a collector plate, where it generates a varying elec-

MAKING FACES ON THE TV SCREEN

PINPOINTING A PICTURE

The face of a clown on the TV screen above has been "drawn" by the pinpoint tip of a beam of electrons sweeping back and forth across the screen in a path like the one below. This pattern shows only 11 such sweeps, whereas the beam actually makes 525 sweeps to fill in the details of the clown's image.

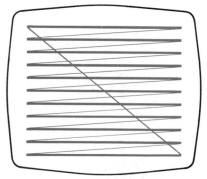

A BEAM OF BUSY ELECTRONS

Unsuspected by the supine television viewer, the world behind his television screen is a hustle and bustle of industrious electrons. Electric pulses representing an image are sent to the cathode of the television picture tube *(left)*. The cathode emits electrons whose flow is regulated by the control grid, speeded up by the accelerating anode, and concentrated into a single beam by the focus anode. This electron beam is then deflected by two sets of electromagnetic coils and made to sweep back and forth across the viewing screen, which is coated on the inside with chemicals that give off light when hit by electrons. After "spraying" the picture on the screen, the electrons are removed through a graphite coating to a high-voltage anode connected by a wire to the outside of the television set.

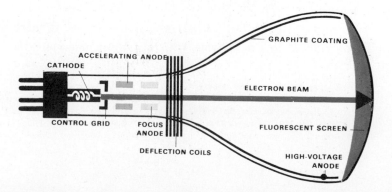

GRAPHITE COATING

ACCELERATING ANODE

CATHODE

ELECTRON BEAM

CONTROL GRID

FOCUS ANODE

DEFLECTION COILS

FLUORESCENT SCREEN

HIGH-VOLTAGE ANODE

tric current. This current provides another electrical representation of the original picture, which is sent along to an amplifier, through the air, to the outstretched, waiting metal arms of rooftop antennae.

In the home television set, the varying current, after detection and amplification, goes to the kinescope, or picture tube. This is roughly pyramidal in shape. At its large end is the familiar fluorescent viewing screen; at its small end is its own electron gun. The beam of the electron gun is focused on the screen and moves across it, causing it to glow. The strength of this beam varies according to the electric signals coming in from the antenna. This variation causes bright and dark spots on the home screen in exact correspondence with the television camera screen, thus re-creating the image from the television studio.

As we watch, in fascination, the arresting replicas of reality on our television screen, there may sit, in the same room, a telephone and a phonograph. On our bedside table stands a radio; another accompanies us in our car. These strange machines never move unless we move them; they come alive only at our touch. But give them their due: they serve us well. They provide the far-flung, trillion-nerved ganglia of commerce, of news, of our mighty military forces. And down through the days and nights of our lives, they ward off our loneliness and bring us nearer together. Perhaps some day they will make us brothers.

The Helping Hand of the Patent Office

Among the powers vested in Congress by the Constitution is one "to promote the Progress of Science . . . by securing for limited Times to . . . Inventors the exclusive Right to their . . . Discoveries." The Patent Office decides whether an inventor merits "the exclusive Right"—or patent—to exclude others from making, selling or using his creation for 17 years in return for making his secrets public. A patent is granted only for an invention which is novel, useful and indeed an invention, not just a new combination of existing devices. These criteria have evolved since 1790, when a grant was issued for a method of making potash, the first of more than three million U.S. patents on machines, products, processes, formulas, designs and plants (chiefly flowers). Many patented inventions never reach the market; others, like the safety razor *(opposite)*, have been produced by the millions, with significant consequences for the nation.

SMALL INVENTION, GIANT IMPACT
King C. Gillette's drawing of his first crude razor with replaceable blades depicts the invention from every angle but the social. That aspect became apparent as beards, mustaches and goatees were stroked off American male faces by Gillette's easy and inexpensive method. During its 17 years of patent protection, Gillette's company built a dominant position in world blade and razor sales.

No. 775,134.

PATENTED NOV. 15, 1904.

K. C. GILLETTE.
RAZOR.
APPLICATION FILED DEC. 3, 1901.

NO MODEL.

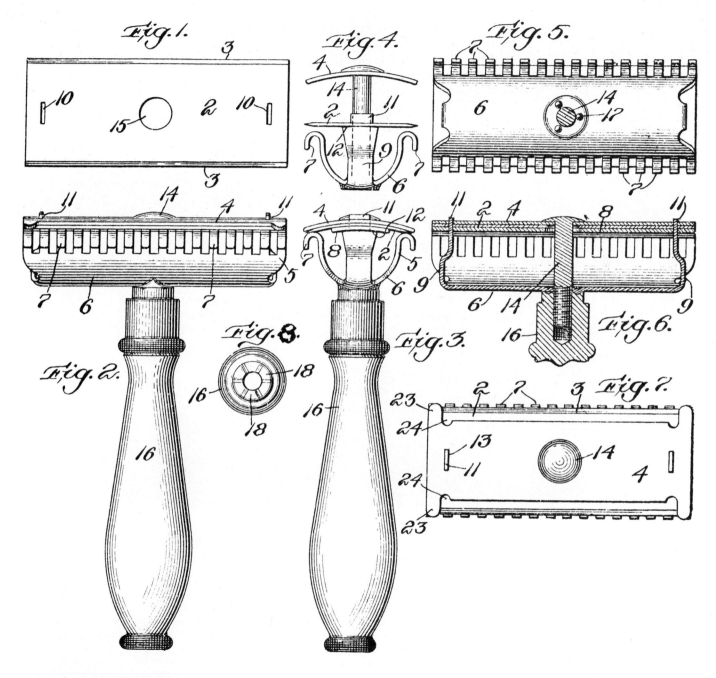

Witnesses:
Ruby M. Banfield
Margaret A. Daniher

Inventor:
King C. Gillette,
by
E. D. Chadwick,
Attorney.

Applications for 85,000 New Inventions Every Year

The big gray colonnaded building above represents a major hurdle for every inventor in the country. It is the Department of Commerce Building in Washington, home for the 2,400 employees of the U.S. Patent Office. To this building every year come the plans of some 85,000 inventions in search of a patent. Anyone may apply and, considering the Patent Office's backlog of 200,000 applications, it sometimes seems to harried officials that anyone does. Neither age, nationality, sex nor technical proficiency is considered in granting a patent, but the procedures (*drawings at right*) are complex enough to cause most inventors to hire a patent attorney or a patent agent to represent them.

Patent attorneys and agents are strictly screened. They must pass a Civil Service examination and meet exacting standards established by the Patent Office. They are not permitted to advertise or seek publicity, for example. Uncomplicated patent applications may cost an inventor from $300 to $500 for professional help, complicated ones $3,000 or more. In addition, the Patent Office fees are at least $60. A patent search (*pages 162, 163*) and competent drawings to accompany the application may run to another $100. If appeals are made to reverse Patent Office decisions, fees and legal costs are increased. Despite the size of the investment, only about half of the 51,000 patents granted each year are commercially developed. Many of them never return the cost of patenting, let alone reap the fortunes optimistically anticipated by their creators.

HOW TO OBTAIN A PATENT

A STRONG, COMMERCIALLY VALUABLE PATENT IS NOT EASILY COME BY. THE INVENTION MUST HAVE GOOD POTENTIAL FOR PROFIT, THE APPLICATION MUST BE CAREFULLY WORDED AND COMPLETE, THE PATENT MUST BE SOLD OR DEVELOPED ASTUTELY. AN INVENTOR IS WISE TO SEEK PROFESSIONAL HELP.

STEP ONE: A PATENTABLE INVENTION IS DEVELOPED.

STEP TWO: ATTORNEY PREPARES AN APPLICATION.

STEP THREE: PATENT OFFICE RECEIVES APPLICATION.

43 OUT OF 100 APPLICATIONS ARE REJECTED, FIVE ARE APPEALED.

57 OUT OF 100 APPLICATIONS ARE APPROVED AND GRANTED PATENTS.

STEP FOUR: PATENT EXAMINER STUDIES APPLICATION.

OF FIVE APPEALS, HALF ARE DROPPED BEFORE HEARING.

ONLY 30 PER CENT OF APPEALS HEARD ARE SUCCESSFUL.

THREE-MAN BOARD HEARS APPEALS.

WHERE PATENTS ARE PROCESSED

The Department of Commerce Building *(above)*, which fronts on Constitution Avenue in Washington, D.C., is home for the U.S. Patent Office. When British troops set fire to the city in 1814, the first Patent Office chief, Dr. William Thornton, persuaded them ''not to burn what would be useful to all mankind.'' His was the only government building not set ablaze.

FOUR STEPS TO A PATENT GRANT

The drawings *(right)* detail the four steps that must be taken before any invention is awarded a patent. From invention to patent can be as short a time as six months or as long as two decades in exceptional cases. General Motors Corporation waited 23 years before its application for a key patent on an automatic choke was finally approved by the Patent Office in 1955.

Elapsed Time from In Basket to Out: Three and a Half Years

Leo Friaglia, 47, has a degree in mechanical engineering and is an expert in land vehicles. Since 1947 he has been an examiner in the Patent Office, one of 1,100 specialists in all fields of technology who have all but the final word on the granting of a patent.

Like his co-workers, Friaglia disposes of about 80 patent applications a year. An application reaches him about a week after it has arrived at the mail clerk's desk *(above)*. That time is consumed by recording and assigning—it is hardly a ripple in the over-all delay. Because of the Patent Office's backlog, Friaglia may not begin his examination of an application for five or six months.

In the course of his study, he will check everything ever patented or published in the general field of the invention to determine its novelty and usefulness. In one case out of 30 he approves an application as submitted by the inventor, and a patent is issued within a few weeks. In the other 29, he rejects one or more of the application's claims and notifies the inventor of the reasons for his decision. The inventor then has six months in which to revise his application or to abandon it. Most inventors revise—as many as three or more times—until Friaglia makes a final rejection or approval. By then, the whole application process may have taken more than three and a half years, two thirds of which may be charged to the delays in the Patent Office.

Sometimes applicants themselves incur delays deliberately. This gives them extra time to develop and market a product under the label "patent pending," so that when the patent is finally issued they may have a sales program well under way.

WHEN ALL THE EVIDENCE IS IN
At his desk, Friaglia studies an application to make certain the invention is clearly and completely described and that every feature of it is depicted in the accompanying drawings. He will reject out-of-hand an invention not legally patentable, such as a new method of doing business, or one that would violate national security, such as a new kind of military weapon.

CONFERENCE FOR DISPUTED CLAIMS
Friaglia confers with his supervisor *(back to camera)* and a patent attorney who has arrived from Milwaukee to settle a patent claim which Friaglia has questioned. The lawyer, who also has a degree in electrical engineering, visits Washington once a month to encourage decisions on pending applications, sometimes bringing samples of new inventions to clarify claims.

Winner's Prize: A Waxed and Ribboned Patent Grant

The gentleman chopping the air in the picture below is a patent attorney telling the judges of the Patent Office Board of Appeals that an examiner did his client wrong by rejecting his application. An appeal is heard by three judges, selected from 15 permanent judges, named by the President, plus 10 others appointed by the Patent Commissioner. Each is a former patent examiner with experience in one or more fields of invention.

The lawyer's argument is a minor factor in their ultimate decision; more pertinent are the original application, the examiner's decisions, the applicant's revisions, prior and related patents, and the reasons given in the applicant's written appeal. The lawyer is not permitted to introduce new evidence or arguments at the hearing; he may seek only to clarify points, in order to reverse the examiner's decision. Examiners themselves are not called to defend their decisions. An appeal costs an inventor $25, plus his attorney's fees. By law an inventor must take his case to the Board of Appeals before carrying it to the federal courts, if he wishes to pursue the matter that far. About 1,000 appeals are filed with the Patent Office each month, but only half of them are carried to a hearing. One reason is that it now takes 12 to 14 months for an appeal to reach the Board. Another is that about 70 per cent of all appeals are rejected, odds that even a nonmathematically inclined inventor understands.

OLD MACHINE FOR NEW PATENTS
Daniel I. Butler, a Patent Office reviewer, operates the 19th Century embossing machine which puts the official seal on a letters patent, the document which is the patent grant. The issuance of letters patent always takes place on Tuesdays at noon. At the same hour, a description and key drawing of the invention are published in the Patent Office's *Official Gazette*.

ARGUMENT FOR THE PLAINTIFF
Judges J. L. Brewrink *(left)*, L. P. McCann and C. D. Angel give their attention to a patent attorney who has exactly 30 minutes in which to argue his client's case for a reversal of a decision. Although the Appeals Board's calendar is filled far in advance, the cases the judges hear represent only one out of 16 applications refused a patent by the Patent Office examiners.

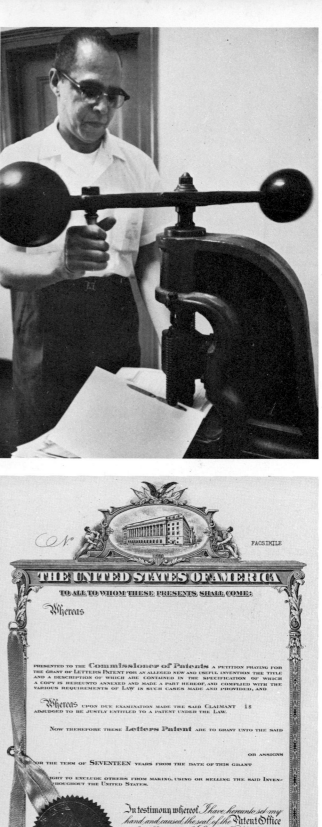

Ribbon and red wax make a letters patent a handsome document.

The Patent Office Search Room offers every U.S. patent since 1836 (when a fire ruined the files) in 308 classes and 59,000 subclasses.

SEARCHING FOR CHEMICAL PATENTS
Donavon Lee Favre, a professional freelance patent searcher, examines a pile of chemical patents. Favre has been a searcher for three years. He holds degrees in chemistry and law, and plans to write his examinations as a patent attorney. He charges clients $5 to $10 per hour.

INVESTIGATING ELECTRICAL PATENTS
A patent attorney from General Electric studies electrical patents for his company's Communication Products Department in Lynchburg, Virginia, a job he undertakes once or twice a year. His search will help ensure that G.E. will not begin or continue work on ideas already patented.

From Patents Past, Hints and Ideas for Patents Future

Since originality is one of the touchstones for issuance of a patent, the search for what may be new under the sun must start with what is old under the roof of the Patent Office Search Room. By mid-morning six days a week the room at left is filled with people seeking patent information. Here, more than three million U.S. and seven million foreign patents are available to the public. Would-be inventors who are unable to travel to Washington can hire professional searchers or do their own looking in one of 22 libraries in the country that have sets of U.S. patents. Or, in lieu of that, they may purchase by mail copies of patents for 25 cents each.

A TREASURE HOUSE OF PATENT LORE
The stacks *(right)* dwarfing the patent searcher in the aisle are two of the dozen 195-foot-long file units which hold copies of more than three million U.S. patents. The copies are checked so often they are printed on special paper to withstand the wear and tear of constant shuffling.

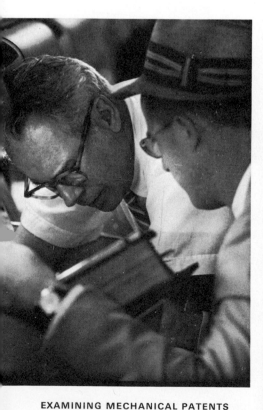

EXAMINING MECHANICAL PATENTS
Richard Wagner scans a file of mechanical patents at another searcher's desk. A Washington freelance searcher, Wagner started at age 19, working for his patent attorney father. He has been 30 years at the work and spends four days a week in the files, one day writing his reports.

Patent Models: Charming Souvenirs of Inventions Past

The requirement that working models accompany patent applications was dropped in 1870. But by 1925, storage costs on previously accumulated models brought on a house cleaning. Some models were distributed to the Smithsonian Institution (which has a fine collection including the four on these pages) and 200,000 were put up at public auction. O. Rundle Gilbert of Garrison, New York, eventually acquired most of them. He shows about 5,000 at a Plymouth, New Hampshire, museum and has 120,000 more in a New York barn. He lacks only a perpetual-motion machine, sole invention for which the Patent Office still insists on seeing a working model.

A STITCH IN A TENTH THE TIME
Elias Howe's 1846 model for a lock-stitch sewing machine *(above)* embodied a basic patent in a new industry. Howe did not make machines at first, but he and Isaac Singer were in the world's first patent pool, which got a $15 fee (later seven dollars) per machine from dozens of firms.

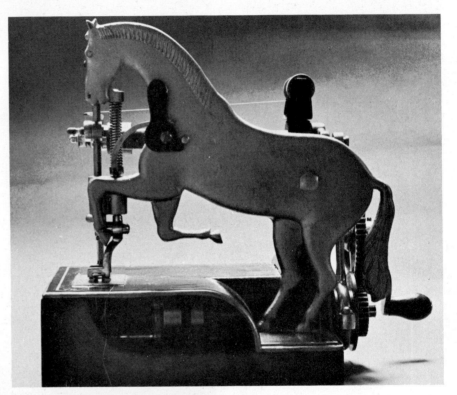

SPEED SYMBOL FOR SEAMSTRESSES
The prancing horse *(right)* adds charm to James Perry's chain-stitch sewing machine of 1858. Perry's method was not covered by the Howe patent, so he could sell his machine cheaply. Unfortunately for sales, though, chain-stitched seams unraveled if a single stitch was broken.

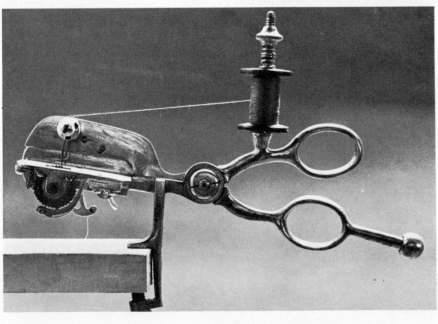

SCISSORS ACTION FOR SEWING
This scissors-like sewing machine *(left)* represents another effort to beat the Howe patent. It was designed to be bolted to a table and operated by working the scissors handle with one hand while feeding the fabric through the machine with the other. It sold for less than $10.

CHERUBIC CHEER FOR HOUSEWIVES
Cherubs symbolically lead the way to sewing bliss with David Clark's 1858 machine *(opposite)*. The hand-cranked device produced a chain stitch. Useless ornaments like these, popular in the 19th Century, usually made machines difficult to operate and were eventually abandoned.

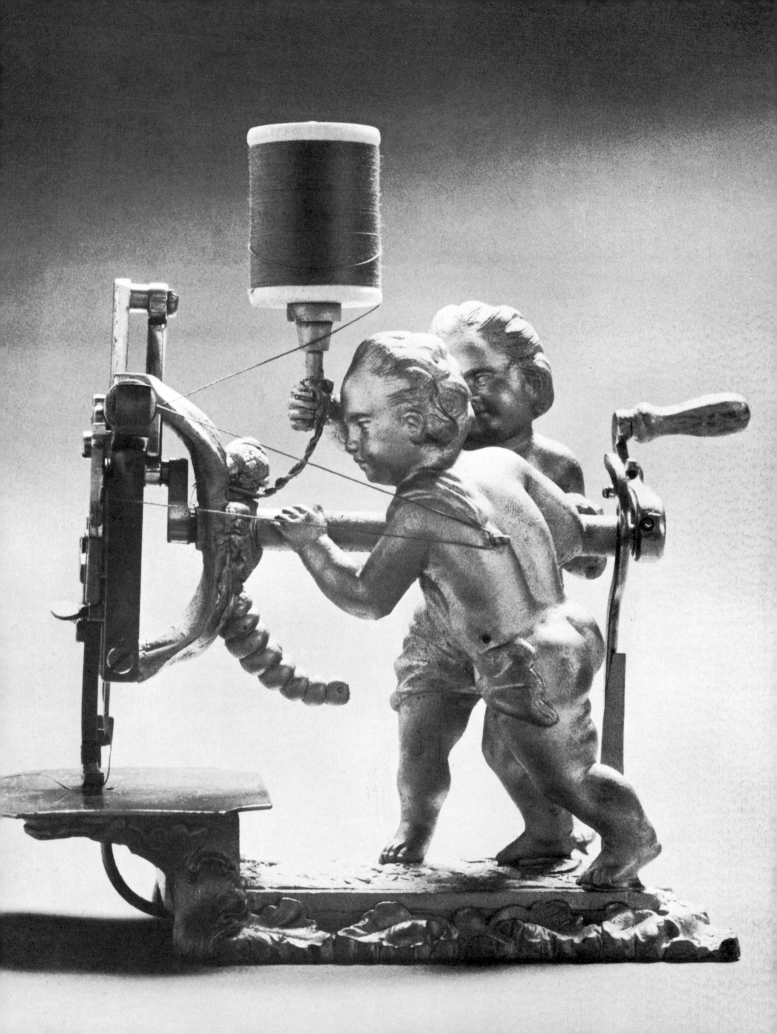

8

The Promise and Problems of Automation

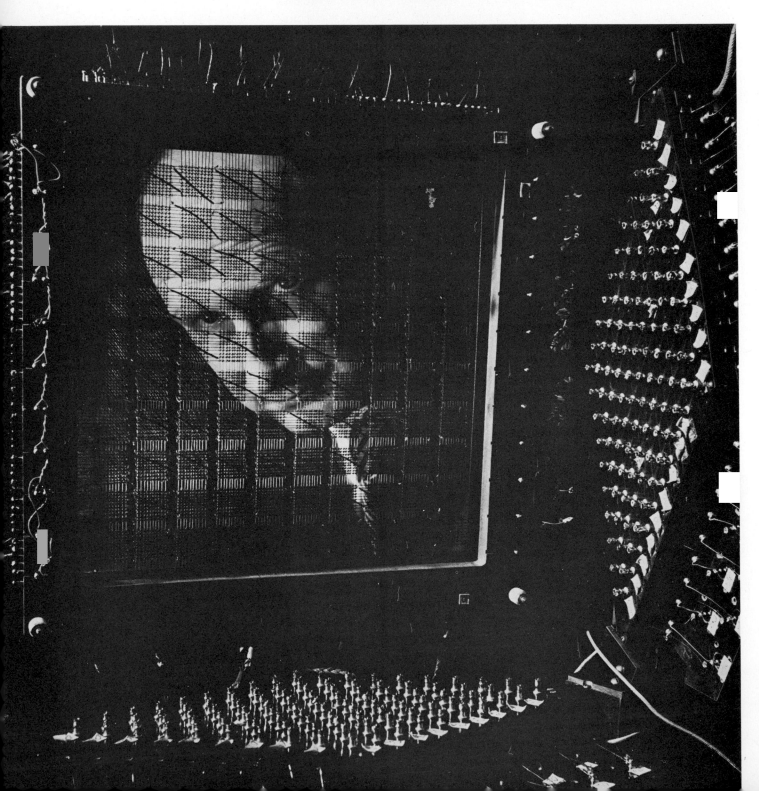

WE HAVE LONG SINCE PASSED THE POINT OF NO RETURN in our relationship with machines. They are essential to our way of life; indeed, they *are* our way of life. And now we have begun to endow them with qualities of our own. We build into their pulsing wires and printed circuits and winking lights the power to think, sense, learn. They have evolved into a veritable community—paper-devourers, wind-streamed travelers, sensors that reveal new worlds in the starry ocean of space and new planets in the invisible universe of the atom. All these toiling robots are our creatures; without them, we should not be quite where we are today. Yet, even as they serve us, they obey inner laws of selection and mutation, born of some kind of self-correcting sense of organization. And so the relationship between us, while it grows ever more interdependent, also produces deeper tensions. It poses questions both disturbing and exciting. Most immediately, it confronts us with the problems—and promise—of automation.

Specialists find it no easier to agree on a definition of automation than on a definition of machines. The word itself, a corruption of "automatization" or "automa-(tic) (opera)-tion," was coined off the cuff about 1935 by Delmar S. Harder, at the time a General Motors plant manager, but it was not widely publicized until more than a decade later. Broadly, automation now encompasses practically any device that reduces the amount of human effort—physical, mental, or both—necessary to do work. In a more specific sense, it means mechanical or electronic control that takes the place of the control function of human brains, human experience and human reflexes.

Greater precision of definition is difficult because there are varying degrees of automation. The automatic washer represents a low degree. We load it, set the controls, switch it on and leave it; it obediently proceeds, by means of a built-in timing system, through its phases of washing, rinsing, spinning; when it reaches the end of the full cycle, it shuts itself off. (A few years ago, appliance stores featured an electric clothes-drier with a music box in its innards that triumphantly played *How Dry I Am* after the drier shut itself off.) The highest degree of automation today appears in digital computers that not only control other machines and their processes but also communicate with them, receive information from them about the process as it is occurring, and use this information to correct or guide the process while it continues. The machines under computer control may be a gang of hot strip steel rollers, the turbo-generators of a regional electric-power grid, or a guided missile speeding at more than four miles a second.

Increasingly, engineers are designing people out of the machine process. The purposes are practical: to eliminate human error, fatigue, boredom; to introduce faster, safer, more economical and consistent methods

MACHINES IN MAN'S IMAGE
In a striking juxtaposition, Dr. Jan Rajchman *(opposite)* peers through his foot-square Myria-bit computer memory unit. When built in 1953, it was the world's biggest core memory, storing 10,000 bits of data. Today miniaturization allows a two-inch-square unit to "remember" 16,000 facts. Such advances presage an era when machines may outdo men in certain skills.

of production; to fulfill the incessant human striving for abundance. And even as their designers toil, the machines themselves seem to be groping more and more toward self-sufficiency, impelled by the same blind will with which a vine climbs toward the sun. The telephone system that began with hand cranks and "Hello" girls is today a marvel of automatic control. In place of the philosophic elevator man who joked about his "ups and downs" is a panel of plastic push buttons.

A new anatomy of machines

All this might well have been foretold, along the line of evolution of machines, by any prophet worth his keep. In the small electric motor, we cut machines loose from main shaft and belt, giving them a separate identity. In steel fingers and cunning joints and electric wires and electronic pulses, we gave them muscles, ligatures and nerves. Eli Whitney's production lines, lavishly elaborated to a phantasmal *ballet mécanique*, continue to pour out rivers of interchangeable parts, and to assemble, package and send them on their endless belts out into the waiting world. Now, however, the eyes that gauge the microscopic tolerances are photoelectric eyes. The hands that hold the workpiece are metal hands. The coordinator of all the intricate ritual of production is a reel of tape or a stack of punched cards—an electronic master animating and directing electronic slaves. Add to the system a computer, and the system thereby acquires the semblance of a brain; a rudimentary brain, to be sure, but one of incalculable swiftness and of implacable logic.

For automation machinery and controls like these, American manufacturers alone spent $8.4 billion in 1963. By 1975, there will be more computer programmers in the United States writing instructions for computers than there will be doctors writing prescriptions for patients. The "trend to automation" is less a trend than a flood tide. Our old world and its familiar things drop astern, like the last Spanish landfall of Columbus as he steered to the Ocean Sea.

The new capability of machines to communicate and control, incredibly accelerated by World War II electronics and weaponry, inspired the eminent Dr. Norbert Wiener, professor of mathematics at M.I.T., to formulate a new discipline devoted to the theory of communication between man and machine, machine and man, machine and machine. He called it cybernetics, derived from the Greek *kybernetes*, or "steersman." It has to do with messages—organized patterns of information, exchanged, primarily, by men and machines. Most messages to the machine are what we should expect such communications to be like—stark, painstaking, spelled-out commands to literal-minded morons. But some, at least to the programmers who compose them, seem struck off with lyric beauty, resembling the geometric cadence of sonnets.

The giving of messages to machines via coded control goes as far back as the textile industry of early 18th Century France. In order to weave a fashionably intricate design into a silk fabric, it was necessary to select and lift certain sets of warp thread, in unison, for the passage of the shuttle. The first device to mechanize this time-consuming drudgery was Basile Bouchon's historic loom, constructed in 1725. Basically, it worked as follows: lines of holes were punched into a roll of paper in accordance with the design to be woven. When this "coded" paper was pressed against a row of needles, those which lined up with the holes remained in place; the others moved forward. The loom's action, as controlled by these selected needles, formed the pattern of the fabric.

Bouchon's machine was the simplest kind of drawloom, with only a single row of needles. But it was the beginning. Improvements soon appeared which made possible drawlooms with several rows of needles activated not by a roll of paper but by narrow, perforated or punched cards strung together in a long belt. The concept behind these devices cast a shadow across the years to the 20th Century: the design was stored in the punched cards just as electronic information for the numerical control of a milling machine, say, in a Burbank aircraft plant, is today stored in a reel of perforated or magnetic tape.

The knowledgeable needle

Building on still further improvements, the French mechanician Joseph Marie Jacquard perfected, about 1804, the classic drawloom action that has remained basically unchanged to this day. Infinitely more complex than Bouchon's system, the Jacquard action controlled as many as 1,200 needles at once. A succession of punched cards was pressed against the bank of needles, one for each pass of the shuttle. Solid parts of the card pushed certain needles back out of the way of the engaging mechanism, but holes in the card allowed other needles to remain in place; a lifting frame raised them and thus raised a corresponding set of warp threads. Only 25 years after Jacquard's first drawloom, 600 of his punched-card-controlled looms, with power supplied by backyard steam engines, were weaving away in the cottages of Coventry alone.

What Bouchon and Jacquard did with their punched paper and cards was, in essence, to provide an effective means of communicating with the loom. The language was limited to just two "words": *hole* and *no hole*. The same binary, or two-based, system is all but universal in today's machine communication. The language of a light bulb, for example, consists simply of *on* and *off*. These two may symbolize whatever man wants them to: *yes/no; go/no go; 1/0*. The vocabulary may be expanded by the use of additional lights and various combinations of *ons* and *offs*. Thus 32 combinations of the *on* and *off* condition of five light bulbs

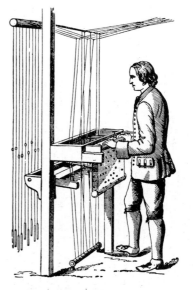

A PATTERN FOR THE FUTURE
The dialogue between men and machines that today has become a garrulous give-and-take began quietly in 1725 when Basile Bouchon, a French engineer, built the loom above, which could weave patterned silk according to instructions coded into a revolving sheet of perforated paper. Bouchon's loom could displace one unskilled laborer (the weaver's apprentice), and so anticipated a problem of modern automation.

are enough to represent the 26 letters of the alphabet, with six left over for punctuation marks.

Instead of lights, modern machine language consists of electric signals or, equally significant, the absence of them. Information in any form—from the plays of Shakespeare to the graph of a curve to the rate of a heartbeat—can be translated into *signal* / *no signal* parlance and fed into a machine. The information fed in is called "input," the product at the other end of the machine process "output," and the rate at which the information travels through the process "throughput." (Thoroughly machine-oriented people do not say they have had too much to eat or drink; they say they suffer from "input overload.")

Postscript to a silk portrait

The first man to think of feeding punched-card information into a machine other than a loom was Charles Babbage, an English mathematician who spent 40 years trying to build an "analytical engine," a mechanical forerunner of the electronic computer. Babbage, a Pickwickian figure in machine history, somehow acquired a five-square-foot, woven-silk portrait of Jacquard himself, fashioned on a Jacquard loom with the aid of 24,000 punched cards, and worked so finely that it resembled a line engraving. This feat is believed to have convinced Babbage that the punched-card system could be applied to his engine; to enable it, in the words of his friend, Ada Augusta, Countess of Lovelace, to weave "algebraic patterns just as the Jacquard loom weaves flowers and leaves." But the Babbage engine foundered on the limitations of a metalworking industry that was simply incapable of engineering the parts Babbage required. He died in 1871, surrounded by the drawings, cogwheels and fragments of his hopeless, half-finished dream. It fell to Dr. Herman Hollerith, a statistician of Buffalo, New York, to make modern man-machine communication a reality.

The U.S. census of 1880, covering a population of 50,262,000, had taken seven years to tabulate. As the 1890 count approached, alarm beset Census Bureau officials. Population had zoomed; how could they compile the new figures within the 10-year limit set by the Constitution? Hollerith averted disaster by devising an ingenious punched-card tabulator. Census information was hand-punched on cards, according to a pre-coded arrangement of positions, or "spots," each representing a separate fact, such as the individual's sex, age, etc. There was one card for each person counted. In the tabulating process, each card was placed over a number of tiny cups filled with mercury. Rows of delicately adjusted pins were brought down on the card. Wherever they encountered a hand-punched hole, they passed through it to the mercury beneath, completing electrical circuits that registered the results on counter dials.

The pins stopped by solid surface registered nothing. Hollerith's tabulator enabled census takers to complete their compilations in just over two years, one third the time of the 1880 count, even though U.S. population had risen more than 25 per cent, to 63,056,000.

The company which Hollerith set up to manufacture his device became, in time, one of the parents of today's goliath International Business Machines Corporation, better known as IBM. In the 70-odd years since the first Hollerith tabulation, methods of communicating with machines have been vastly refined. Specially trained people called "programmers" translate instructions into symbolic language that is in turn electronically spelled out in binary vocabulary within the machine. The machine's circuitry shunts the electric pulses through to their destinations, at a rate as high as a million or more a second, just as boxcars are shunted through a maze of freight-yard trackage. The switch in the path of the pulses is open or closed, permitting them through or deflecting them. The rigid, inflexible, two-word language of machines brooks no overtones, no leap of fancy, no margin for error—simply *yes* or *no*, *on* or *off*, *open* or *closed*, *1* or *0*.

Information is fed to today's machines in one of three principal ways: by punched card, by punched tape made of paper or plastic, or by magnetic tape. (Another medium is magnetic ink, used primarily by banks in processing checks.)

A hole full of meaning

Standard punched cards are perforated either automatically or by a manually operated keyboard machine resembling a typewriter, which can make a small round or rectangular hole at any one of hundreds of positions on the card. In the particular user's code, a position may signify a number, a letter, a date, a location on a blueprint, a point on a curve, a temperature reading, a certain bin in a warehouse. Punched tape is prepared in similar fashion. Its positions run lengthwise along the tape in as many as eight parallel channels, and information is recorded on it by holes punched in meaningful combinations. Machines receive the messages of the holes through built-in "reading devices," which sense the holes' presence, convert them into electric pulses and flash them on into the circuitry. According to the type of reading device used, card-reading speed usually ranges from 100 to 1,000 cards a minute, tape-reading speed from 150 to 500 perforations a second.

The magnetic tape used in machine communication is similar to tape used in home recorders, except that it is usually a half inch instead of a quarter-inch wide and carries seven channels instead of two or four. Each channel is divided into spots, or "bits"—sometimes as many as 800 per inch of tape—which correspond to the positions on cards or paper tape.

KEYS TO UNLOCK A CHINESE PUZZLE

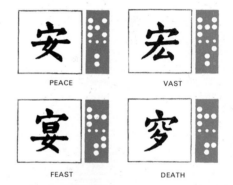

PEACE   VAST

FEAST   DEATH

TRANSLATION IN A TRICE

An electric keyboard hooked up to a computer can translate one language into another once both are put on tape in binary code.
To translate a complex Chinese character into English, the operator reduces it to simpler components. He presses one key *(below, left)* containing one part of the character *(shaded area)*, then a second key containing another part. All Chinese characters with such components flash onto a screen. Among these characters—four are shown above —the operator notes the numerical position of the one he is translating, and presses another key numbered to correspond to that position. This starts the coded tape *(above, at characters' right)* through a computer memory store of English. The matching word, "vast," is eventually printed on an "output sheet."

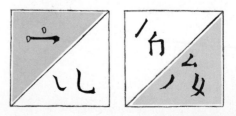

171

Information is recorded on the tape by magnetizing these bits with a set of electromagnetic heads. In the input process, the magnetized bits travel past a reading device that converts them into the language of electric pulses at speeds as dazzling as 630,000 bits per second.

These electromechanical means of communicating with the machine have enabled us to replace human steersmen with mechanical steersmen, human sense organs with electronic sensors, human brains with computers. Machines, in short, increasingly run themselves, bringing close indeed a utopia glimpsed as long ago as the Fourth Century B.C. by Aristotle: "If every instrument could accomplish its own work, obeying or anticipating the will of others . . . if the shuttle would weave and the pick touch the lyre without a hand to guide them, chief workmen would not need servants, nor masters slaves."

Clockwork and control

Man has built two basic kinds of control into his machines. One, known as "open-loop control," makes it possible for a machine, once started, to proceed as if by clockwork through a pre-established pattern of performance. The other, called "closed-loop control," or, more familiarly, "feedback," makes it possible for a machine to check, correct and control its own operations while they are in progress.

Neither type of control is new to the age of electronics. Hero of Alexandria, some 2,000 years back, created a simple, cause-and-effect, open-loop control when he devised a linkage of expanding hot air, water, bucket, spindles and counterweight, that swung open the doors of a temple when a priest lighted a fire on a nearby altar (left). In the 18th Century, James Watt used a classic feedback control to maintain the desired speed of his steam engine. Metal balls were mounted on a revolving shaft geared to the engine's main output shaft. When speed began building up, centrifugal force caused the spinning balls to lift upward and outward, like airplane swings on a carnival ride. As they did so, they partially closed the throttle, thus reducing the speed of the engine. A drop in speed below the desired level produced the reverse effect.

Open-loop controls abound in today's machines—in the start-to-stop performance of an automatic washing machine, an automatic record changer, a coffee-vending machine. But the heart and soul of full automation, of the most advanced stage of the man-machine relationship, is the dynamic, self-correcting, self-regulating dominion of feedback.

Feedback devices maintain desired standards of machine performance by generating what control engineers call the "error signal"—in effect, supplying answers to the machine's question, "How am I doing?" An example may be seen in the simple thermostatic furnace control. A thermostat is set at 72°F. If the room temperature drops below that, the

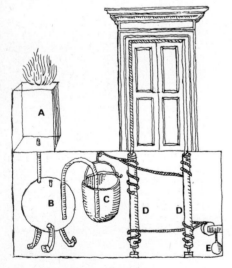

AN AUTOMATED DOORMAN

Almost two millennia ago, Hero's temple-door opener used built-in machine controls. A fire on a hollow altar (A) raised air pressure within, forcing some of the water stored in a hollow sphere (B) through a siphon into a bucket (C). As the bucket dropped, it pulled ropes attached to pivots (D), which swung open the doors. When the fire died and air pressure became normal, a falling counterweight (E) shut the door.

thermostatic sensor feeds back an error signal; the thermostat kicks on the furnace; the temperature rises to the desired level, and the thermostat shuts off the furnace. The relationship of furnace to room temperature to thermostat and back to furnace is direct, interacting, closed, as in a chain or loop—hence the term closed-loop control.

Although feedback control devices were known two centuries ago, they began to come into their own in the 1920s. This breakthrough was neither isolated nor overnight. It could not have happened without the vacuum tube to amplify and relay the sensors' feeble signals. It could not have happened without advances in the sensors themselves—without transducers for sensing pressures, temperatures, forces, velocities, volumes of light and sound; without detectors for spotting overheat, overload, moisture, flow—all the clever, bioelectronic devices that enable a machine to hear and see, touch and feel. Nor would the breakthrough have taken place so long before anyone really expected it without the technological thrust of World War II, that evolved brilliant uses of feedback in automatic detection, in tracking and firing systems of all kinds, and, above all, in the proximity fuze, whose radar feedback exploded its shell the instant it came within a set distance of its target.

The kingdom of feedback

Today feedback is at work on every hand, automating processes that are vital to our health and comfort as well as to the nation's economy. It regulates the flow of electricity in our power lines, maintains the quality of our oil and gasoline, our steel, copper and concrete, and ensures the consistency of many foods and drugs. It has had particular impact on the sprawling, 156-billion-dollar-a-year metalworking industry, because it has made possible self-regulating automatic control—called "numerical control" by the industry—of machine-tool operations.

Numerical control—described by one study group as "the touchword of a manufacturing revolution"—guides a machine through its task, without human intervention, simply by means of numerically coded instructions fed into the machine. A routine machine-shop job, for example, called for the drilling of 100 evenly spaced holes with a prescribed accuracy of 0.005 inch. Layout and drilling by hand took eight hours. With the use of numerical control, the entire operation, from programming to the finish of impeccably drilled holes, took just 56 minutes. And besides drilling, other operations now possible under numerical control include riveting, milling, bending and grinding.

The monarch of today's machine marvels, however, is the computer. Even as early machines extended man's muscles and more recent machines his senses, computers extend his mind. They calculate and compute, add, subtract, multiply, divide—and give the answers with speed

SOMETHING NEW IN THE WIND

For centuries mills were at the mercy of winds which could idle them by changing direction. In 1745, Edmund Lee, an Englishman, built an automatic control into a mill *(above)* in the form of a "fantail," a set of vanes fixed at right angles to the sails that kept them facing into the wind. The fantail was connected by gears to wheels running on a track at the base of the mill tower, thus permitting the tower to turn with the breeze.

173

and effortless accuracy. They are the first machines that we are making our junior partners, so to speak, in the management and exploration of the world we live in.

Although computers have come into use only since the end of World War II, they have already rescued commerce and business from a rising flood of paperwork and enabled management to lend new immediacy to its decisions. By their capacity to store and retrieve data, they help to control the postwar proliferation of scientific and technological findings sometimes called "The Information Explosion." More than 200 of them flawlessly control manufacturing processes in chemical plants, oil refineries, and steel, paper and cement mills. Never has one machine stirred so much excitement; it has been called the most promising and powerful achievement in machine history since the assembly line.

An electronic brontosaur

The world's first all-electronic computer went into operation in 1946, at the Moore School of Electrical Engineering of the University of Pennsylvania. An enormous and brontosaurian device known as ENIAC, it had been designed and built under pressure of U.S. Army needs for computing trajectories for new weapons. Like most computers to follow, it had a name formed from the initial letters of its full designation, Electronic Numerical Integrator and Calculator.

ENIAC, invented by two researchers at the University of Pennsylvania, J. Presper Eckert, an electronics engineer, and Dr. John W. Mauchly, a mathematician, sprawled over 1,500 square feet, weighed about 30 tons, contained some 18,000 vacuum tubes and had a capacity representing a few thousand nerve cells—biologically the equivalent of the brain of a flatworm. An ENIAC with the 10-billion-cell capacity of the human brain would have occupied a building larger than Britain's Houses of Parliament, and would have required a Niagara Falls to power it. Nevertheless, ENIAC was nimble enough to do, in 30 seconds, work that took an ordinary calculator 20 hours.

Today the bulk of ENIAC reposes in a warehouse. Its descendants in the U.S. alone, some 16,000 strong, click and blink away in quiet, air-conditioned rooms in government offices, in banks, in campus laboratories, in the headquarters of corporations of all sizes. They bear little resemblance to ENIAC. The trim, clean-lined and often pastel-shaded cabinets, consoles and printers of small units would fit comfortably inside an apartment-house kitchen. Old-fashioned wiring has given way to printed-circuit panels; the venerable vacuum tube has yielded to the transistor, which, some statistics-lover has figured out, consumes less energy than a jumping flea.

There are two kinds of computer: analog, from the Greek *analogos*, or

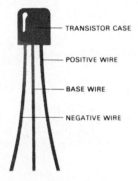

THE POWER BEHIND BOTH TINY RADIOS AND HUGE COMPUTERS

TRANSISTOR CASE

POSITIVE WIRE

BASE WIRE

NEGATIVE WIRE

A MAGNIFICENT MITE
Small, durable and emitting little heat, the transistor *(above)* makes possible tiny marvels like pocket radios because, like the bulkier vacuum tube, it has the power to amplify. In moving from the first to last of the transistor's three sections *(below)*, a steady flow of current from a negative wire turns into a fluctuating signal, amplified up to 40,000 times and emitted through a positive wire. A small weak signal injected by a base wire into the second section effects this change.

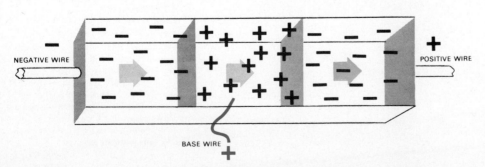

NEGATIVE WIRE

POSITIVE WIRE

BASE WIRE

"proportionate"; and digital, from the Latin *digitus*, or "finger," so named for the practice of computing with our fingers. Analog computers deal not in numbers but in analogous physical quantities. The information with which they are presented is couched in physical rather than numerical terms—electric voltage, angle of rotation of a shaft, etc.—and the answers they come up with are likewise expressed in physical terms. (The speedometer on a car is a simple analog device, converting a shaft's rate of turning into mile-an-hour terms.) Digital machines, which vastly outnumber the analog variety, literally calculate and compute. Their basic output is numbers. They live on electric pulses, millions every second; these are coded in the binary system—numbers *1* or *0*—and fed into the machine via punched cards, punched tape or magnetic tape.

These computers have five elements—input devices, control unit, storage unit, processing unit and output devices. Their operation may be compared to the way we handle a simple problem in arithmetic. Input is the information provided in the problem. Control represents the arithmetical rules that guide us in working out the problem. Storage is our knowledge both of numbers and of the answers to intermediate steps en route to the solution. Processing is akin to our paper-and-pencil figuring of the problem. Output is the final answer.

The pace of a junior partner

The comparison is, necessarily, a primitive one. A large-scale computer can keep more than a million bits of data in its memory and can turn out work faster than 500,000 men using, not pencil and paper, but desk calculators. Because of this, its range as man's collaborator is unlimited. It advises New England apple-growers on optimal harvesting periods just as effortlessly as it enables automobile manufacturers to satisfy buyers' orders for optional equipment without interruption to the assembly-line process. It compiles mixing formulas for cattle and poultry-feed manufacturers in Mexico and New Zealand as efficiently as it helps doctors in Cincinnati plan radiation dosages for cancer patients. It helps predict the weather, translates Russian scientific papers, keeps track of ships at sea, and takes off man's hands and mind thousands of humdrum but useful and essential tasks.

What lies ahead? Not even computers can answer this question. But computer design is following two paths. One leads to ever faster, more specialized machines; the other leads to machines even more and more like people. Computers are being taught to learn. An IBM physicist, for example, has taught an IBM 704 to play checkers. He programmed it to avoid making the same mistake twice, to improve, to get better. Ultimately, it defeated him.

Others are attempting to design "biological computers" that will be able to accept and integrate several kinds of input at once, to display the adaptiveness of a living animal. So far, most of the studies have been devoted largely to "pattern-recognition" devices based on the light-sensitivity of photoelectric cells. An experimental IBM device named Shoebox recognizes up to 16 spoken words, including 10 digits and such arithmetical code words as "plus," "minus" and "total." When told to do so, Shoebox relays simple problems to an adding machine and instructs it to print out the answers.

These devices, today, are experimental. Some will lead to new machines; others will trail off to nowhere. Whatever their future, they do not alter the nature of our long and eventful relationship with machines. For thousands of years, machines have been helping us mold and shape the world to which we were born. Now, for the first time, they are taking over tasks that we have heretofore accomplished with our own brains. And all at once, they confront us with mountains to climb—the challenge of learning how to use machines fully and to our best advantage, the even higher challenge of discovering ways in which to use the priceless manpower they displace. But in the struggle up the slopes, we shall earn a better understanding of ourselves, a deeper communion with each other and each other's needs. And from the summit, new lands will beckon, brighter by far than those we have known.

The New Industrial Revolution

The word "automation" is charged with emotion. To some people it brings a dream of new leisure, new skills and new freedom. To others it brings a nightmare of dislocation and shattered patterns of work. For automation denotes nothing less than a sweeping new Industrial Revolution, born of machines that "think" and of new human attitudes toward manufacture of goods and the management of business. The pages that follow provide a probing look into the nooks and crannies of American industry, revealing how far toward an automated society we have already moved, whether in terms of power plants that practically run themselves or of commercial kitchens that bake cakes automatically. The revolution has reached far and wide since that day in 1946 when Delmar S. Harder, then a Ford Motor Company vice president, remarked, "Give us some more of that automatic business. . . . Some more of that 'automation.'"

AN AUTOMATED BOWL OF SOUP
The white-capped workman opposite is one of the two "chefs" who monitor the mixing of Knorr soups in a five-story automated plant at Argo, Illinois. The plant "foreman," a brainlike console, directs other machines to weigh and mix some 40 ingredients with such precision that the fragile dried vegetables do not break and the fats do not congeal into a gummy mass.

FEEDBACK FROM FLYBALLS

The governor *(left)* on a skyscraper elevator is the same machine as the "flyball governor" used by James Watt in 1788 to maintain the speed of a steam engine. If the engine went too fast, the outward swing of the rotating balls closed the throttle, and vice versa. This is called "feedback"—a machine keeping in touch with, and adjusting to, its own work.

CUSTOM CARS IN MASS PRODUCTION

At General Motors' Willow Run "body bank" near Detroit *(above)*, new models clamped to monorails start down the assembly line. Data-processing equipment is used to schedule a production line so flexible that the plant can turn out more than 240,000 cars a year without making any two identical as to color, body style, engine and optional equipment.

MACHINES PLAYING THE NUMBERS

In much the same fashion that player pianos are run by coded piano-rolls, a modern metal-drilling machine, such as the Tape-O-Matic at left, takes its cue from a numerical blueprint coded on perforated tape. Among this machine's virtues are precision, cheapness ($11,000) and versatility: simply change the tape and Tape-O-Matic drills a new set of holes to order.

The Multitudinous Meanings of Automation

"Automation" is a blanket word, almost an American colloquialism for technological progress. Even among engineers the word is never very precise, and covers all kinds of mechanical contrivances and electronic hookups. Yet, although these devices differ from each other in operating principle, in appearance and in purpose, all of them involve some degree of self-regulation or control. For, in order to be truly automated, a machine must somehow respond to its own senses.

A modern guided missile is perhaps the most awesome example of automation, for here automatic instruments replace a human crew, and the whole machine is sensitive enough to its direction and speed to anticipate the need for corrections carried out in flight. But automation touches us more immediately in the very warmth of our homes, where the thermostat on the wall senses changes in room temperature and starts up or shuts down the furnace to keep the house evenly heated.

The pictures on these pages illustrate the diversity of even simple automated mechanisms. The "flyball governor" that slows an elevator when it starts to plummet (opposite, top) bears little relation to the Tape-O-Matic device that drills metal on instructions from coded tapes (opposite, bottom). Yet these are as much "automation" as are the tireless automobile assembly lines (above) in Detroit.

When Machines Become Vice Presidents

Electronic control is more suited to the processing of liquid products than to the production of hard goods. So it is natural that the "flow" industries—oil, chemicals and electric power, for example—are automating on an unprecedented scale.

The spick-and-span oil refinery at Tyler, Texas *(above)*, represents a first step toward a fully automated plant. Here, a mas-ter control panel records a mass of data from every part of the plant, and shows the three technicians what adjustments to make and where. In even more advanced plants, computers replace the technicians and instruct automated machines to make adjustments. In effect, only the mathematicians who program the computers and the mechanics who repair the

instruments need tend the mammoth. Such plants already exist. And businessmen foresee a time when whole corporations will be automated, when computers in remote plants will report costs, sales and inventories to a control center. Then, making market forecasts and watching the competition, computers may make decisions up to the vice-presidential level.

REFINING OIL BY PUSH BUTTONS
Three operators man the automatic controls *(foreground)* that guide all production at a 360-acre oil refinery in Tyler, Texas. Here, at the Texas Eastern Transmission Corporation, crude oil (some 17,000 barrels a day) is turned into premium motor oil, aviation gasoline and other petroleum products. The operators, to qualify for such work, need only a high school education.

The "Brain" behind the Telephone

Touch a telephone and the world's biggest computer is at your finger tips—a multi-billion-dollar, continent-sized complex of senders, markers, links, coaxial cables, switches, and an endless roster of other electronic and mechanical components.

In the coast-to-coast direct-dialing network of the Bell Telephone System, automation has reached almost unfathomable proportions. The instant an instrument is dialed, the sprawling system is at work locating the desired number—one among more than 82 million U.S. telephones—choosing one of the several open paths to reach it and making the connection.

When someone in New York places a call to San Francisco, hundreds of relays go into a conference in Manhattan, crossbar switches snap in Sacramento, signal tubes pulse in Oakland, a sender hustles in San Francisco, a marker grabs an idle circuit and a telephone rings. As many as 100,000 moving parts may be involved in the call. Furthermore, the split-second

decisions of this mechanical intellect are its own: no human knows what routes a call took to reach its destination.

Bracing for the future, Bell engineers are now replacing moving parts with the newest electronic devices. This spruced-up system will automatically diagnose its own defects, tell repairmen where to find them and reprogram itself to circumvent breakdowns. Even the men building this burgeoning goliath, says one, "are hard put to visualize it in its full dimensions."

CALLING BY COMPUTER

The 17th floor of the Bell Telephone System's long-distance equipment center in New York City houses hundreds of tons of built-in intelligence, watched over by three men. This LD center is one of 69 (another 16 are planned by 1970) now spotted in cities and towns throughout the United States. Without this kind of automation, it would take nearly every working woman in the U.S. to handle the phone calls, local and long-distance, made in a single year.

No Machine Yet for Spreading the Mustard

Even the humble hot dog has been automated. At Oscar Mayer and Company, the nation's largest wiener and bologna producer, the age-old *wurstmacher*'s art has been converted into a modern science. The company's engineers have linked many existing machines in unique ways, created other machines from scratch, added automatic controls and devised a new system to waft the wiener on its way from meat grinder to supermarket.

Where once the wieners were painstakingly hand-stuffed, smoked, cooled and then wrapped, electronic and automatic equipment *(opposite and below)* now handles the job. One machine, for example, pinches the casings to make wieners of standard length. Another later strips and removes this artificial skin. Still others wrap and vacuum-seal the wieners in a saran-plastic package. Such automation is spreading throughout the food industries, and is now contemplated in distribution and retailing. In 10 years packaged foods may move from warehouse to market, be priced and displayed, all by machine. The housewife will purchase by push button and pay at an automated check-out.

HOT DOGS IN HIGH GEAR

Ten lanes at a time, wieners are whisked down an automated production line at the Oscar Mayer plant in Madison, Wisconsin. The machine shown opposite turns out 25,000 finished frankfurters an hour; coming up is a 36,000-an-hour model. Mayer's automated wieners are made in one continuous process, going from raw meat to saran-wrapped package in a mere 36 minutes.

PRECISION-MADE WIENERS

Dials on a control console *(above)* tell a technician exactly what is happening to the wieners that are zipping past, unaided by human chefs. If even slight errors occur anywhere along the production line, a flashing light on the control panel summons a mechanic. Besides being faster, automated processing makes wieners of uniform color, texture, flavor, shape and length.

Who's in the Kitchen with Honeywell 610?

Cakes from the Kitchens of Sara Lee are among the tastiest items to come from data-processing devices. And a computer now bakes them in quantities that even Sara Lee did not dream of 10 years ago.

In the spanking new automated kitchens at Deerfield, Illinois, a giant Honeywell 610 computer, capable of 62,500 computations a second, is doing the brainwork of the world's biggest baking operation. Each day it turns some 36,000 pounds of milk, 66,000 pounds of whole eggs, 90,000 pounds of topgrade butter and similar magnitudes of other ingredients into countless cakes of 12 varieties, storing them automatically on the shelves, in a warehouse as big as a football field.

Machines take over the moment ingredients arrive at the plant, pumping and packing them into storerooms: 36 million pounds of flour and sugar, for example, are kept on hand. Each morning, handed a production schedule, the computer takes stock, sorts out its recipes, rolls up its sleeves and goes to work. Soon machines are batch-blending, mixing and baking. Icing is added, cakes are quick-frozen, foil pans are covered—and the packages are off to the warehouse within an hour after they leave the oven.

But Sara Lee has not abolished the human element in baking. Quite the contrary, says the company's president: "Automation is employed only as a tool to assist . . . bakers in doing a better job." Moreover, all the butter for Sara Lee's "all butter" cakes is still added by hand.

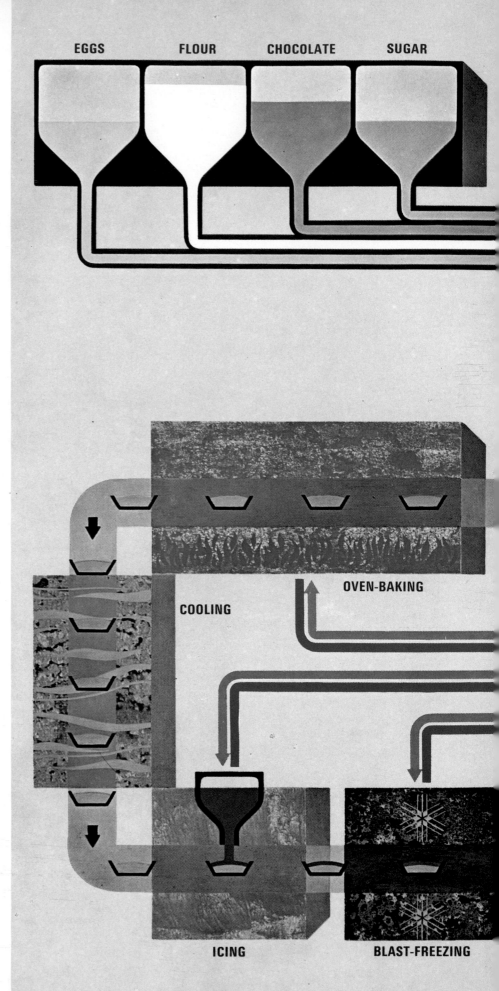

EGGS   FLOUR   CHOCOLATE   SUGAR

OVEN-BAKING

COOLING

ICING   BLAST-FREEZING

A COMPUTER'S KITCHENWARE

At the Kitchens of Sara Lee, represented in the diagram on these pages, one computer *(below)* masterminds the baking of 12 varieties of cake. It watches some 300 variables in the cake-making process and scans reports from its sensors at the rate of 200 a second. If a correction is needed, the computer types it out and sounds an alarm to summon a baker.

MIXING

1 SCHEDULING The control operator feeds the computer a production schedule each morning, indicating the cakes needed that day. The computer then checks the Kitchens' stocks to be sure that all needed ingredients are on hand.

2 MIXING The computer sees that ingredients are added in the right amount and the right sequence. It eventually will be taught to make allowance, in its recipes, for the dampness of flour and the solids content of eggs. At the right moment it signals an operator to add butter and such trace ingredients as vanilla, salt and yeast.

3 BAKING The computer keeps a sharp eye on the cakes as they move by conveyor belt through a 110-foot oven. By monitoring speed and temperature, the computer controls the baking time.

4 ICING After the cakes have cooled, they are decoratively iced by machine: the computer makes sure the icing mixture is uniform. It also keeps count of cakes that pass inspection.

5 FREEZING Before packaging, the computer sends the cakes by conveyor belt through a 35-foot "blast freezer," a chamber chilled to −40° F.

6 WAREHOUSING Ready to hold nearly eight million cakes, the warehouse is automatically run on a first-in, first-out basis. After computer-operated stacker cranes retrieve pallets to fill shipping orders, the brain sends billing information to the business office. Every 15 seconds the computer revises and updates its "memory."

HONEYWELL 610

SHIPPING

PACKAGING   WAREHOUSING

Increased Output and Idle Hands

The 50-ton metal milling machine (*right*) at the Bendix Corporation in South Bend, Indiana, is limited solely by the imagination of engineers. Instructed by taped directions, it is turning aluminum forgings into landing-gear struts for Phantom II, the Air Force's fastest, highest-flying fighter-bomber. "But every week," says a Bendix man, "our engineers learn new things they can do with it." This mammoth metalworker and its computer have greatly increased productivity at Bendix (*caption, below*) while the nature of workmanship has changed.

The mushrooming of machines with electronic intelligence has brought a spectacular rise in productivity throughout American industry. Operating a keyboard or push-button panel, punching numbers in tape or dropping IBM cards in a slot, workmen can now do more work in less time than ever before. To man the new machines, many former "blue collar" workers have acquired new skills and turned "white collar." But many other people have been "automated out of work." A single glass plant with 14 workers, for instance, can now produce 90 per cent of the electric light bulbs used in the U.S., as well as all the radio and television tubes—picture tubes excepted.

Thus, as words like "cybernetics," "servomechanism" and "automation" spell out a bright industrial future, phrases like "chronic joblessness" and "pockets of unemployment" present a great human challenge. For the ingenious minds that have devised a machine to do the work of 60 men must now find ways to retrain, relocate and restore work to the displaced.

THE PRICE OF PRODUCTIVITY
Making aircraft landing-gear cylinders (suspended in foreground of the photograph, *right*) and other precision parts, the milling machine at the Bendix Corporation makes each worker more productive. Formerly, the five men at top left —toolmaker, product designer, tool designer, set-up man and machine operator—made four landing gears a day. Now the nine men at top right who work this machine—the original five along with four computer specialists—can turn out 12 gears a day. On balance, six jobs have been "lost" in a day's production of 12 gears.

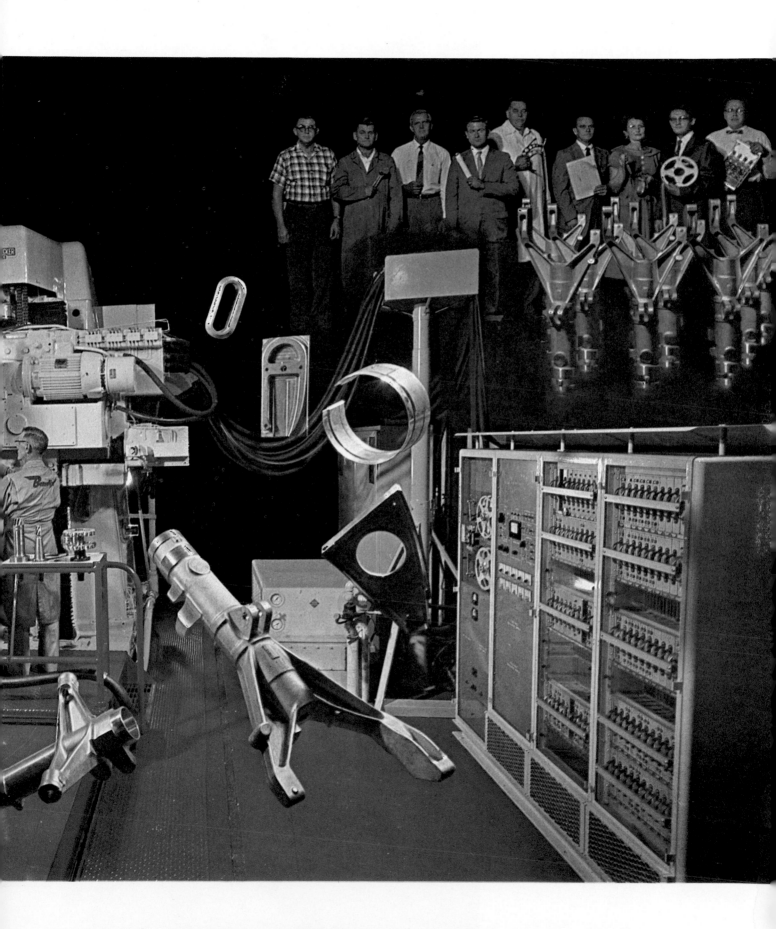

Mighty Machines That Transformed an Archaic Industry

Nowhere are the effects of automation more clearly evident than in the soft-coal industry, which in the mid-1960s began showing signs of healthy growth after more than a decade of decline.

The huge preparation plant at Moss No. 3 *(right)* is a symbol of automation's part in this revival. "It wouldn't have paid to open without mechanized mining equipment and an automatic system to clean and grade the coal," says a Clinchfield Coal Company Division executive.

Such an operation also symbolizes the economic decline of the old-fashioned coal digger. In 1947, the U.S. had 450,000 miners. In 1963, there were 119,000 and they used new skills to operate massive machines and earned nearly twice as much as in 1947. The all-out mechanization has more than doubled U.S. soft-coal productivity since World War II. The new average was about 15 tons a day per miner.

Economists and labor experts differ on just how many jobs are lost to such changes in technology. One widely quoted estimate from the U.S. Department of Labor in 1962 was nearly 8,000 a workday.

Like coal company managers, other businessmen are concerned, but feel there is no alternative to machines. "It is no longer a question of whether or not to automate," says an electrical manufacturer. "If you don't, your competitor will."

COAL A LA CARTE
Control-panel lights reflect in the glass enclosure of the preparation plant *(right)* at Pittston Company's Moss No. 3 mine in Virginia. The largest and most automated coal mine in the U.S., it taps a rich but high-waste seam. One man *(above)* controls 90 per cent of the process that cleans raw coal and separates high-grade from low. Such technology typifies the industry's new energy. "The coal mines would have shriveled up without automation," says Consolidation Coal Company's board chairman George H. Love, who led the move to modern ways.

A Chronicle of Human Ingenuity

The history of machines is the story of man's constant search for better, faster and easier ways to accomplish his work. The table below lists some important inventions of the past 50 centuries. From this tabulation two important facts emerge: that while invention is a continuous process, it is not an even and orderly march of progress but a series of dramatic spurts followed by relatively barren interludes; and, most important, that America's rise to leadership of the world has been paralleled and assisted by the thrust of U.S. inventiveness.

It is no coincidence that the entry "American" occurs with increasing regularity in the "Nationality" column until, from the 1900s on, it dominates. Of 44 major inventions of the 20th Century, 38 are American: the political, intellectual and economic forces that forged the young nation were the same forces that prodded it to technological excellence.

FROM LEVERS AND LATHES TO MODERN TECHNOLOGY

DATE	MACHINE	INVENTOR	NATIONALITY
Paleolithic Age	lever, wedge, inclined plane	unknown	unknown
c. 3000 B.C.	wheel and axle	unknown	unknown
c. 3000 B.C.	sail	unknown	Egyptian
8th Cent. B.C.	pulley	unknown	Assyrian
3rd Cent. B.C.	water screw, block and tackle	Archimedes	Greek
3rd Cent. B.C.	pump	Ctesibius	Greek
2nd Cent. B.C.	lathe	unknown	unknown
1st Cent. B.C.	horizontal waterwheel	unknown	Mesopotamian
1st Cent. B.C.	vertical waterwheel	unknown	Roman
7th Cent. A.D.	horizontal windmill	unknown	Persian
c. 9th Cent.	crank and flywheel	unknown	unknown
1185	vertical windmill	unknown	English
c. 12th Cent.	trebuchet	unknown	unknown
1298	spinning wheel	unknown	German
c. 1300	cannon	unknown	unknown
1335	mechanical clock	unknown	Italian
c. 1448	printing press using movable type	Johann Gutenberg	German
c. 1500	rifle	unknown	German or Austrian
c. 1520	wheel-lock firearm	unknown	German
c. 1589	knitting machine	William Lee	English
early 1600s	breech-loading firearm	unknown	Italian
c. 1615	flintlock firearm	unknown	unknown
1642	adding machine	Blaise Pascal	French
1654	air pump	Otto von Guericke	German
1656	pendulum clock	Christian Huygens	Dutch
1698	steam pump	Thomas Savery	English
1712	steam engine	Thomas Newcomen	English
1733	flying shuttle	John Kay	English
1765	condensing steam engine	James Watt	Scottish
1767	spinning jenny	James Hargreaves	English
1769	steam-driven tractor	N. Joseph Cugnot	French
1769	water frame spinning machine	Richard Arkwright	English
1776	submarine ("Bushnell's turtle")	David Bushnell	American
1779	spinning mule	Samuel Crompton	English
1783	gas balloon	J. E. and E. M. Montgolfier	French
1784	puddling iron furnace	Henry Cort	English
1786	power loom	Edmund Cartwright	English
1786	threshing machine	Andrew Meikle	Scottish
1786	nail-making machine	Ezekiel Reed	American
1790	steamboat	John Fitch	American
1790	machine for cutting nails	Jacob Perkins	American
1793	cotton gin	Eli Whitney	American

DATE	MACHINE	INVENTOR	NATIONALITY
1795	hydraulic press	Joseph Bramah	English
1797	cast-iron plow	Charles Newbold	American
1798	papermaking machine	Nicolas-Louis Robert	French
1800	engine lathe	Henry Maudslay	English
1804	steam locomotive	Richard Trevithick	English
1804	Jacquard loom for figured-weaving	Joseph Marie Jacquard	French
1807	wood-mortising machine	Marc I. Brunel	French
1807	commercially successful steamboat	Robert Fulton	American
1809	carbon arc light	Sir Humphry Davy	English
1810	mowing machine	Peter Gaillard	American
1811	steam-powered printing press	Friedrich Koenig	German
1816	circular knitting machine	Marc I. Brunel	French
1818	profile lathe	Thomas Blanchard	American
1819	cast-iron plow (modern shape)	Jethro Wood	American
1820	cultivator	Henry Burden	American
1820	rubber shredder	Thomas Hancock	English
1822	electric motor	Michael Faraday	English
1822	calculating machine	Charles Babbage	English
1824	pin-making machine	L. W. Wright	American
1825	commercially successful steam locomotive	George Stephenson	English
1826	photography	Joseph N. Niépce	French
1827	water turbine	Benoît Fourneyron	French
1831	dynamo	Michael Faraday	English
1834	reaper	Cyrus H. McCormick	American
1834	ice machine	Jacob Perkins	American
1835	revolver	Samuel Colt	American
1835	steam shovel	William S. Otis	American
1837	telegraph	Samuel F. B. Morse	American
1837	steel plow	John Deere	American
1839	steam hammer	James Nasmyth	Scottish
1840	bicycle	Kirkpatrick MacMillan	Scottish
1846	sewing machine	Elias Howe	American
1847	rotary printing press	Richard M. Hoe	American
1849	Francis turbine	James B. Francis	American
1849	turret lathe	Frederick W. Howe, Richard S. Lawrence, Henry D. Stone	American
1850	grain binder	John E. Heath	American
1851	washing machine	James T. King	American
1856	steel converter	William Kelly, Sir Henry Bessemer	American English
1857	open-hearth steelmaking furnace	Frederick and William Siemens	English
1857	shoe-sewing machine	Lyman R. Blake	American
1857	passenger elevator	Elisha G. Otis	American
1860	internal-combustion engine	Étienne Lenoir	French
1862	universal milling machine	Joseph R. Brown	American
1865	pin-tumbler cylinder lock	Linus Yale Jr.	American
1867	typewriter	Christopher L. Sholes, Carlos Glidden, Samuel W. Soulé	American
1869	railway air brake	George Westinghouse Jr.	American
1869	vacuum cleaner	Ives W. McGaffey	American
1871	pneumatic drill	Simon Ingersoll	American
1876	telephone	Alexander Graham Bell	American
1876	four-cycle gas engine (Otto engine)	Nikolaus August Otto, Eugen Langen	German
1877	phonograph	Thomas A. Edison	American
1879	automatic screw machine	C. W. Parker	English
1879	cash register	James Ritty	American
1881	electric streetcar	Werner von Siemens	German
1882	electric iron	Henry W. Seely	American
1882	electric fan	Schuyler S. Wheeler	American
1884	Linotype machine	Ottmar Mergenthaler	German-American

DATE	MACHINE	INVENTOR	NATIONALITY
1884	steam turbine	Sir Charles A. Parsons	English
1885	automobile	Karl Benz	German
1885	Dictaphone	Charles S. Tainter	American
1887	Monotype machine	Talbert Lanston	American
1888	motion picture camera	E. J. Marey	French
1890	punched-card tabulator	Dr. Herman Hollerith	American
1891	motion picture projector	Thomas A. Edison	American
1892	diesel engine	Rudolf Diesel	German
1894	automatic loom	James H. Northrop	American
1895	electric locomotive	unknown	American
1896	radio telegraph	Guglielmo Marconi	Italian
1896	electric stove	William S. Hadaway Jr.	American
1899	magnetic recorder	Valdemar Poulsen	Danish
1900	electric-powered submarine	John P. Holland	American
1900	photocopy machine	Rene Graffin	French
1901	radiotelephone	Reginald A. Fessenden	American
1903	airplane	Orville and Wilbur Wright	American
1903	bottlemaking machine	Michael Owens	American
1905	track-laying tractor	Benjamin Holt	American
1907	electric vacuum cleaner	James M. Spangler	American
1907	electric washing machine	Alva J. Fisher	American
1911	automobile self-starter	Charles F. Kettering	American
1911	combine	Benjamin Holt	American
1911	air conditioning	Willis H. Carrier	American
1913	refrigerator	A. H. Goss	American
1913	talking motion pictures	Thomas A. Edison	American
1915	radiation therapy machine	Friedrich Dessauer	German
1918	automatic toaster	Charles Strite	American
1923	television (iconoscope electronic scanner)	Vladimir K. Zworykin	American
1923	bulldozer	unknown	American
1924	diesel electric locomotive	Hermann Lemp	American
1925	all-electric phonograph	J. P. Maxfield	American
1926	liquid-fuel rocket	Dr. Robert H. Goddard	American
1928	mechanical computer	Dr. Vannevar Bush	American
1928	television (image pickup tube)	Philo T. Farnsworth	American
1928	electric shaver	Jacob Schick	American
1928	mechanical cotton picker	John Rust	American
1930	jet-propulsion engine	Frank Whittle	English
1932	earth scraper	Robert G. LeTourneau	American
1933	FM radio	Edwin Howard Armstrong	American
1935	mechanical garbage disposer	William Merrill	American
1936	radar	Sir Robert A. Watson-Watt	English
1938	xerography	Chester Carlson	American
1938	automatic clothes drier	J. Ross Moore	American
1939	helicopter	Igor Sikorsky	American
1942	nuclear reactor	Enrico Fermi	Italian-American
1943	artificial kidney machine	Dr. Willem Kolff	Dutch
1943	electrical discharge machine tools	B. R. and N. I. Lazarenko	Russian
1945	phototypesetting machine	E. G. Klingberg, Fritz Stadelmann, H. R. Freund	American
1946	ENIAC electronic computer	J. Presper Eckert, John W. Mauchly	American
1947	continuous coal miner	Harold F. Silver	American
1952	numerically controlled machine tooling	Frank Stuelen	American
1953	heart-lung machine	Dr. John H. Gibbon	American
1954	solar battery	Gerald L. Pearson, Daryl M. Chapin, Calvin S. Fuller	American
1954	maser	Dr. Charles Townes	American
1957	thermionic (heat to electricity) converter	Dr. Volney C. Wilson	American
1963	commercial gas-turbine automobile	George Huebner Jr. and team	American

BIBLIOGRAPHY

Historical

Ashton, T. S., *The Industrial Revolution, 1760-1830.* Oxford University Press, 1948.

*Burlingame, Roger, *Machines That Built America.* Harcourt, Brace and World, 1953.

Davidson, Marshall B., *Life in America.* Houghton Mifflin, 1951.

DeCamp, L. Sprague, *The Heroic Age of American Invention.* Doubleday, 1961.

Derry, T. K., and Trevor I. Williams, *A Short History of Technology.* Oxford University Press, 1961.

Dunham, Arthur Louis, *The Industrial Revolution in France, 1815-1848.* Exposition Press, 1955.

Eco, Umberto, and G. B. Zorzoli, *A Pictorial History of Inventions.* Macmillan, 1963.

Finch, James Kip, *The Story of Engineering.* Doubleday, 1960.

Giedion, Siegfried, *Mechanization Takes Command.* Oxford University Press, 1948.

Henderson, W. O., *The Industrial Revolution in Europe, 1815-1914.* Quadrangle Books, 1961.

*Kirby, Richard S., Sidney Withington, Arthur B. Darling and Frederick G. Kilgour, *Engineering in History.* McGraw-Hill, 1956.

Lilley, S., *Men, Machines and History.* Cobbett Press, London, 1948.

†Mantoux, Paul Joseph, *The Industrial Revolution in the Eighteenth Century.* Harper & Row, 1961.

†Usher, Abbott Payson, *A History of Mechanical Inventions.* Beacon Press, 1959.

White, Lynn Jr., *Medieval Technology and Social Change.* Oxford University Press, 1962.

Biography

Chamberlain, John, and the Editors of FORTUNE, *The Enterprising Americans.* Harper & Row, 1961.

*Editors of FORTUNE, *Great American Scientists.* Prentice-Hall, 1961.

†Flexner, James T., *Inventors in Action: The Story of the Steamboat.* Collier, 1962.

Fuller, Edmund, *Tinkers and Genius.* Hastings House, 1955.

Green, Constance McL., *Eli Whitney and the Birth of American Technology.* Little, Brown, 1956.

†Josephson, Matthew, *Edison.* McGraw-Hill, 1963.

Leithäuser, Joachim G., *Inventors' Progress.* World, 1959.

†Mirsky, Jeannette, and Allan Nevins, *The World of Eli Whitney.* Collier, 1962.

Rolt, L.T.C., *The Railway Revolution; George and Robert Stephenson.* St. Martin's Press, 1962.

Special Fields

Brady, Robert A., *Organization, Automation and Society: The Scientific Revolution in Industry.* University of California Press, 1961.

*Dunlop, John T., *Automation and Technological Change.* Prentice-Hall, 1962.

Koff, Richard M., *How Does It Work?* Doubleday, 1961.

Kursh, Harry, *Inside the U.S. Patent Office.* W. W. Norton, 1959.

Lewis, Floyd A., *The Incandescent Light.* Shorewood, 1961.

Nosow, Sigmund, and William H. Form, *Man, Work and Society.* Basic Books, 1962.

Pfeiffer, John, *The Thinking Machine.* J. B. Lippincott, 1962.

Postley, John A., *Computers and People,* McGraw-Hill, 1960.

Vennard, Edwin, *The Electric Power Business.* McGraw-Hill, 1962.

*Wiener, Norbert, *The Human Use of Human Beings.* Houghton Mifflin, 1950.

*Also available in paperback edition.

†Only available in paperback edition.

ACKNOWLEDGMENTS

The editors of this book are especially indebted to Frederick G. Kilgour, Librarian of the Medical Library, Yale University, who served as general consultant, and to the following persons and institutions who helped in the preparation of the book: Dr. Torsten Althin, Director, *Tekniska Museet,* Stockholm; Albert K. Baragwanath, Curator of Prints and Paintings, Museum of the City of New York; Sylvio A. Bedini, Curator, Department of Engineering, Smithsonian Institution; Dr. Charles K. Bockelman, Associate Professor of Physics, Yale University; Hsien-Wu Chang and J. M. Kinn, IBM Watson Research Center, Yorktown Heights, New York; John M. D'Albora, Department of Electrical Engineering, Columbia University; Bern Dibner, Curator, The Burndy Library, Norwalk, Connecticut; Herman Diehl, H. L. Diehl Company, South Willington, Connecticut; D. F. Dietzen and W. R. Pitt, IBM; Dr. Robert Ehrlich, Head of Transportation Research Group, Davidson Laboratory, Stevens Institute of Technology; Isaac Fleischmann, Director of Information Services, U.S. Patent Office; Dr. Harry Gray, Associate Professor of Chemistry, Columbia University; Jack Harned, General Motors; Grant N. Horne, Associate Editor, Edison Electric Institute; Romana Jarwitz, Picture Collection, Elisabeth E. Roth, Print Collection, Lewis M. Stark, Rare Books, New York Public Library; William A. Johnson, Director of the Department of Religion, Drew University; Robert H. Jones, General Electric News Bureau; Mrs. Herbert Keller and Paul Vanderbilt, Wisconsin State Historical Society, Madison; Oliver K. Kelley, Director of Engineering Development Department, General Motors Technical Center, Warren, Michigan; Daniel MacMaster, Director, Museum of Science and Industry, Chicago; Sterling F. McIlhany, Lecturer, School of Visual Arts, New York City; Dr. David Miller, Director of Laboratories, American Machine and Foundry Company, Springdale, Connecticut; Dr. Helmut Nickel, Assistant Curator, Arms and Armor Division, Metropolitan Museum of Art; James Ogle, Plant Manager, Toastmaster Company, Elgin, Illinois; James L. Paul, American Telephone and Telegraph Company; Lynn Perkins and Harry Williams, Western Electric Company; Glenn Puncochar and George A. Stauter, Minneapolis-Honeywell Regulator Company; Mrs. Mary Frances Rhymer, Curator of Prints, Chicago Historical Society; William Richards, Director of Museum Bureaus, Pennsylvania State Museum, Harrisburg; Sy Seidman; Norman R. Speiden, Curator, Edison National Historic Site, West Orange, New Jersey; and Milton A. Walsh of the Radio Corporation of America.

INDEX

Numerals in italics indicate a photograph or painting of the subject mentioned.

PICTURE CREDITS

PRODUCTION STAFF FOR TIME INCORPORATED

Arthur R. Murphy Jr. (Vice President and Director of Production), Robert E. Foy, James P. Menton and Caroline Ferri
Text photocomposed under the direction of Albert J. Dunn and Arthur J. Dunn

Printed by R. R. Donnelley & Sons Company, Crawfordsville, Indiana,
and Livermore and Knight Co., a division of Printing Corporation of America, Providence, Rhode Island
Bound by R. R. Donnelley & Sons Company, Crawfordsville, Indiana
Paper by The Mead Corporation, Dayton, Ohio